A Field Guide to the

Monterey Bay Aquarium

MONTEREY BAY AQUARIUM®

886 CANNERY ROW, MONTEREY, CA 93940-1085
TELEPHONE (831)648-4800 FAX (831)648-4810
www.mbayaq.org

The mission of the

Monterey Bay Aquarium

is to inspire conservation

of the oceans.

ACKNOWLEDGMENTS

We'd like to thank Judy Rand and the
many exhibit developers and staff writers who
brought the Monterey Bay Aquarium to life. We'd also like
to thank Dr. Steven Webster and Susan Blake
for their efforts in reviewing this book.

Published in the United States by the Monterey Bay Aquarium Foundation,
886 Cannery Row, Monterey, CA 93940-1085. www.mbayaq.org

Library of Congress Cataloging in Publication Data:
A Field Guide to the Monterey Bay Aquarium
p. cm.
Includes index.
ISBN 1-878244-21-3 (pbk.)
1. Monterey Bay Aquarium—Guidebooks. 2. Marine aquariums,
Public—California—Monterey—Guidebooks. 3. Marine organisms-
-California—Monterey Bay. I Title.
QL79.U62M655 1998
597'.07'379476—dc21   98-36560
                                                                CIP
Managing Editor: Nora L. Deans
Project Editor: Lisa M. Tooker
Editor: Michelle McKenzie
Designer: Elizabeth Watson

Cover Credits: (Front Cover) Jeff Foott/sea otter, Monterey Bay Aquarium/kelp;
(Back Cover) Ann Caudle/Monterey Bay Aquarium/jellyfish

Printed on recycled paper in Hong Kong by Global Interprint

CONTENTS

Monterey Bay Habitats: Nearshore Galleries

Monterey Bay Habitats: Outer Bay Galleries

Welcome to the hidden world of Monterey Bay—a spectacular ocean realm at the heart of the nation's largest marine sanctuary. Our exhibits are home to ocean creatures that live right here in Monterey Bay. The exhibits recreate the bay's habitats, from shallow tide pools to the open sea.

From the deep reefs to the rocky shore, each part of Monterey Bay is distinct, its characters molded both by physical factors and the plants and animals living there.

The timeless forces of sand, wind and wave … the clashing of Earth's massive plates … the constant pull of the tides … all create the living places we call habitats.

Each creature lives in a habitat that suits its needs, and is marvelously adapted to survive the stresses there. And each also plays a vital role in the larger community, where all lives intertwine in a web of feeding and breeding.

Monterey Bay has many faces. Come closer and see.

MONTEREY BAY HABITATS

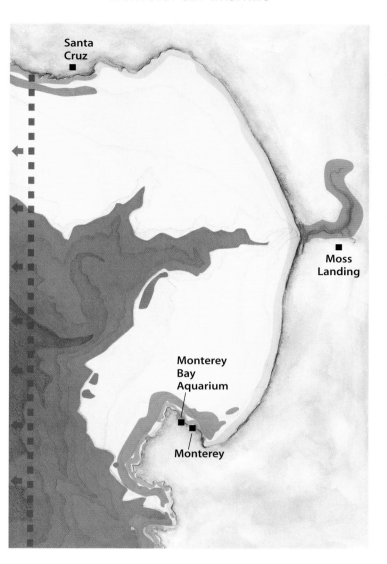

The Kelp Forest

The Deep Reefs

The Sandy Seafloor

The Shale Reefs

The Slough

The Sandy Shore (Aviary)

The Rocky Shore

The Outer Bay

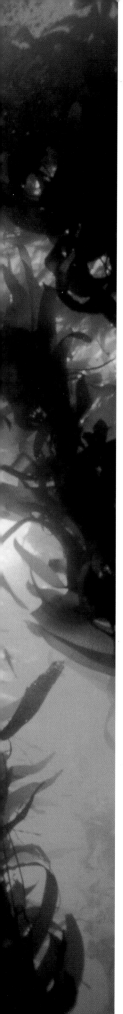

The Kelp Forest

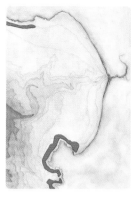

Off the Monterey coast beyond the pounding breakers, where light speckles the seafloor, grow the giant kelps.

Groves of waving kelp form a sheltered, sun-dappled forest

Holding fast to the rocky bottom, the huge pliant plants grow upward, then spread their fronds across the water, creating a dense canopy. This ceiling leaks sunlight, illuminating schools of rockfishes and perch as they swim below.

Down in the plant's tangled holdfast, a crowded community of crabs and others hides from roving fishes. Camouflaged kelpfishes nestle in the thick carpet of plants and animals covering the rocks. And wedged out of reach in cracks are urchins and abalones.

Like land forests, the kelp forest changes with the seasons. Winter waves rip the plants from their rocks and fling them onto beaches, thinning the forest. In spring, the plants fill in the gaps. Unfurling quickly, new fronds grow ten inches a day, till a fresh canopy arches overhead. From the sheltering canopy to the haven of the holdfast, these giant plants nourish and protect dwellers at every level.

Blue top snail
Calliostoma ligatum

◄ *The kelp forest is a haven for many invertebrates, fishes and marine mammals.*

9

The Kelp Forest

BLADES

Many of the kelp's blades spread across the surface of the water. There, they gather sunlight for photosynthesis, the process of changing solar energy into sugars.

Bryozoans find a temporary space

The white crust growing on a kelp blade is actually a colony of tiny animals called bryozoans. The blades make a good base while they last, but take the bryozoans with them when they wear or tear away.

CANOPY

The matted kelp canopy absorbs wave shock, making this a calm spot in rough seas. Otters take advantage of the refuge, as do shorebirds, which forage among the fronds.

FRONDS

Numerous fronds grow from each holdfast. Although a single holdfast may live as long as seven years, fronds are more fragile, usually pulling loose within six months.

Fishes pick at tiny kelp crawlers

Kelp fronds make a high-rise haven for many small invertebrates. Tucked among the stipes and blades, these creatures make favored pickings for many kelp forest fishes.

FLOATS

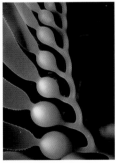

These gas-filled bulbs act as floats to buoy the kelp. Sometimes the floats do their job too well, pulling anchor in the surge so that the plants drift away, rock, holdfast and all.

STIPE

The stipe is this plant's stem. It is strong enough to entangle the propellers of unwary boats, yet has the flexibility to whip back and forth in the surge without breaking.

HOLDFAST

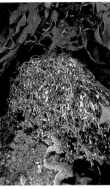

Rootlike, but not a root, the holdfast anchors kelp firmly to the rocks. It can withstand wave surges the equivalent of 126 mph winds—which is holding fast, indeed. Kelp holdfasts provide high-density housing for crabs, worms, urchins and assorted other creatures.

Rocks make kelp forest foundations

Rocks both anchor and protect forest dwellers. Plants and plantlike animals attach firmly to their surfaces, while fishes and other creatures hide in the crevices.

Sea grapes
Botryocladia pseudodichotoma

Life thrives in the kelp beds

From the deep reefs to rocky shores, each part of Monterey Bay is distinct, its character molded both by physical factors and by the plants and animals living there.

Giant kelp grows on sunlit rocky reefs, where cold water constantly washes its fronds. It forms vast groves in the bay and, with associated plants and animals, makes a unique habitat—the kelp forest.

In this forest, kelp is king

Giant kelp influences everything that lives beneath it. The plants stand like a windbreak to rolling Pacific waves, and their close-spaced fronds help screen animals from hungry predators.

Kelp feeds its entire community. Kelp crabs and snails nibble the live plants, or feed on dead, drifting pieces. Fishes nibble the nibblers in turn. And while the thick canopy gives sea otters a nap-time anchor, its shade prevents many algae from growing below.

This is a forest of many faces

Within the kelp forest community are smaller neighborhoods, each attracting its own residents. Shallow, sunny expanses encourage seaweeds to spring up. On deeper, darker rocks, the algae give way to a mossy turf of attached animals.

Sandy channels offer plants no foothold, but many animals can dig in. The forest floor harbors secretive sculpins, while schooling rockfishes swim up among the fronds.

The Kelp Forest

Sheephead
Semicossyphus pulcher

The smaller sheephead are all rosy young females. When a female grows to twelve inches or more, she may become a red, white and black male—depending on how many other males are already prowling about.

diet: sea urchins, other invertebrates
size: to 1 ft. (30.5 cm)

Giant green anemone
Anthopleura xanthogrammica

This green plantlike creature is actually an animal with plants living inside it. Algae in the tissues of the anemone's gut provide extra nourishment and a bright green color.

diet: mussels, crabs, small fishes
size: to 1 ft. (30 cm)

Pacific sardine
Sardinops sagax

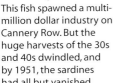

This fish spawned a multi-million dollar industry on Cannery Row. But the huge harvests of the 30s and 40s dwindled, and by 1951, the sardines had all but vanished. Today, only a few schools enter the bay.

diet: small plankton
size: to 15 in. (39 cm)
habitat: small oval cans

Pterygophora
Pterygophora californica

Thickets of this seaweed can form a dense canopy four to five feet above the kelp forest floor. The darkness under the canopy discourages many of the sun-loving red algae from growing there.

size: to 6.5 ft. (2 m)

Sheephead
Semicossyphus pulcher

Ever ready to defend his turf, a male sheephead wears his colors to warn others away. Big buckteeth make him look even fiercer, though they're not used for attack so much as for lunch.

diet: crabs, other invertebrates
size: to 3 ft. (1 m)

Giant kelp
Macrocystis pyrifera

Stands of giant kelp along this coast form the most extensive underwater forests in the world. Living anchored to rocks 20–100 feet deep, the big plants can grow ten inches a day, or more.

size: to 150 ft. (46 m)

Señorita
Oxyjulis californica

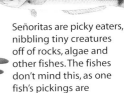

Señoritas are picky eaters, nibbling tiny creatures off of rocks, algae and other fishes. The fishes don't mind this, as one fish's pickings are another fish's parasites.

diet: small invertebrates
size: to 10 in. (25 cm)

Striped surfperch
Embiotoca lateralis

With its bright orange and blue stripes, this surfperch is one of the most colorful fishes found along the entire North Pacific coast.

diet: small crustaceans, worms, mussels
size: to 15 in. (38 cm)

Horn shark
Heterodontus francisci

While sleeker sharks rule the open waters, flat lumpy ones fit in better on the bottom. Wedged under ledges, holed up in caves, or matching the floor's decor, horn sharks hide by day so they'll live to feed at night.

diet: crustaceans, sea urchins
size: to 4 ft. (1.2 m)

Turkish towel
Chondracanthus corymbifera

The rough leathery fronds of this plant gave it the name "Turkish towel." Those warty bumps house thousands of tiny spores, a seaweed's version of seeds.

size: to 39 in. (1 m)

Treefish
Sebastes serriceps

A treefish acts like a jealous property-owner. Defending the rocky crevice where it lives and hunts, the fish chases off trespassers with open mouth and wide-spread fins.

diet: invertebrates, small fishes
size: to 16 in. (41 cm)

Blue rockfish
Sebastes mystinus

Large groups of blue rockfish congregate in the kelp forest in summer and fall, then disappear for the rest of the year. We're not sure why they leave, but it's probably to spawn.

diet: jellyfishes, crustaceans, fishes
size: to 21 in. (53 cm)

Halfmoon
Medialuna californiensis

A silvery, shining halfmoon orbits close to the kelp beds. Counting on kelp for food and protection, it eats both the plant and the creatures that crawl among its fronds.

diet: kelp, other algae, crustaceans
size: to 19 in. (48 cm)

Garibaldi
Hypsypops rubicunda

Garibaldis are a rare sight this far north. The orange means "Caution: this fish defends its turf." That includes a shelter hole, feeding area and, in summer, a nest of eggs.

diet: sponges, bryozoans, worms
size: to 14 in. (36 cm)

Copper rockfish
Sebastes caurinus

Keep a lookout for the copper stationed just above the rocky floor. Rather than patrol open water, this fish hovers, watching the prey go by.

diet: crustaceans, fishes, molluscs
size: to 21.5 in. (55 cm)

Kelp rockfish
Sebastes atrovirens

This fish often hangs upside down and motionless near kelp. Because it won't swim off when divers approach, it's called the "dumb bass," but perhaps that's just smart camouflage.

diet: small crustaceans, squids, fishes
size: to 17 in. (43 cm)

Rubberlip surfperch
Rhacochilus toxotes

Why does this surfperch have the large, rubbery lips that inspired its name? Marine biologists don't really know—can you think of a reason?

diet: crabs, shrimps, molluscs
size: to 16 in. (41 cm)

Kelp greenling
Hexagrammos decagrammus

With these fishes, it's easy to tell the girls from the boys. The female's larger, with orange spots, while the male's spots are bright blue. During mating season, the blue spots grow even brighter.

diet: worms, crustaceans, small fishes
size: to 2 ft. (61 cm)

This is a forest of many faces

A closer look at the kelp forest community reveals smaller neighborhoods, each with its own mix of residents.

SHALLOW TURF

In the sunlit shallows, green, brown and red algae thrive. They carpet the rocks with a thick turf of varied shapes and textures. Crabs, snails and other animals find shelter among the fronds.

KELP PLANT

From holdfast to canopy, the kelp plant is home to many animals. Brittle stars, worms and shrimp crowd the holdfast. Top snails and turban snails stick to the stipes. And giant kelpfish and tiny hydroids find shelter among the fronds.

GRANITE REEF

Cracks and crevices in the granite provide shelter for abalones, urchins, sea stars, fishes and octopuses. And kelp plants anchor themselves to the solid rock.

WATER COLUMN

Many kinds of fishes frequent this part of the forest. Schools of jackmackerel weave through stands of kelp, then flash through sunlit, open spaces. Señoritas dart here and there. And rockfishes hover all around: near the kelp, by the bottom and in the open.

VERTICAL FACES

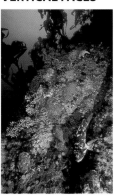

Far more animals than plants cling to vertical rock faces (although some of the animals look like plants). Fields of flowerlike strawberry anemones, forests of branched hydrocorals and bushy colonies of bryozoans grow here along with sponges, tunicates and cup corals.

SAND CHANNEL

Loose sand offers little to hold onto, so plants and many animals can't anchor here. But the channel's not barren. Burrowing anemones and worms dig into the sand. Camouflaged flatfishes rest on the surface, while bat stars and gumboot chitons cruise across it.

DEEP TURF

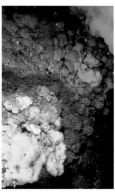

In deeper, darker water, attached animals dominate the turf. Anemones, sponges and tunicates cover the rocks. Red algae (which can grow with less light than their green or brown cousins) grow among the animals.

◄ *Blue rockfish*

Join a kelp forest dive

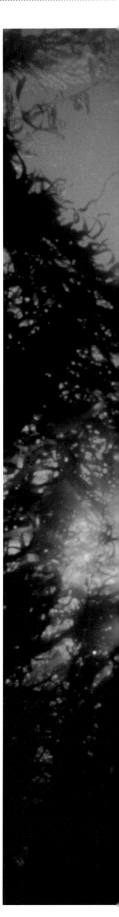

"My diving buddy and I arrived early for our kelp forest dive . . .

. . . From the beach, we swam out to where the giant kelp canopy made a rough patch on the water's surface. Then, giving each other the 'let's go' sign, we dove."

"I swam up along a granite reef . . .

. . . spending a long time peering into its crevice. Each was jammed with crabs, abalones and sea stars. A monkeyface-eel glared at me from one crevice, and a rockfish hovered in another. The rock's surface was covered with life, too— besides hiding animals, the reef anchors the plants, like a solid base for the kelp community."

Sheep crab
Loxorhynchus grandis

Sea cucumber
Parastichopus parvimensis

Black-and-yellow rockfish
Sebastes chrysomelas

The Kelp Forest

Over the shallow turf

"I found a seaweed carpet . . .

. . . It was red, brown and green algae, different shapes and kinds. Sun danced down through the water, making patterns of light on the seaweeds, and a strong surge kept them in constant motion. At first, I didn't see any animals, but running my hand through the algae, I scattered crabs and other creatures that had been hiding."

—notes from a kelp forest dive

Decorator crab
Loxorhynchus crispatus

Sea grapes
Botryocladia pseudodichotoma

Red coralline algae
Corallina officinalis

By the deep turf

"I dove deeper into the forest . . .

. . . As the light grew dim, the green and brown seaweeds that love sun were replaced by a garden of red algae and attached animals— anemones, tunicates, sponges. The further down I swam, the less I felt the surface influences of waves and sun. The constant surge calmed, the water grew colder, and in the dusk at this depth, even bright colors faded to blue-green or gray."

—notes from a kelp forest dive

Jeweled top snail
Calliostoma annulatum

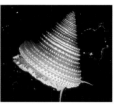

Chestnut cowry
Cypraea spadicea

Turkish towel
Chondracanthus corymbifera

Crevice kelpfish
Gibbonsia montereyensis

The Kelp Forest

Over the sand channel

"A sandy trail ran between the boulders ...

...on the kelp forest floor. As we swam, my partner's flippers kicked up sand flurries—and I realized why loose sand was no place for an animal to hang on. But the area wasn't as barren as it looked. I passed over burrowing worms, camouflaged flatfishes hugging the sand, and a gumboot chiton so big, the surge didn't budge it."

—notes from a kelp forest dive

Blackeye goby
Coryphopterus nicholsii

Gumboot chiton
Cryptochiton stelleri

Blue rockfish
Sebastes mystinus

Rainbow surfperch
Hypsurus caryi

Along vertical rock faces

"I swam up along another rock ...

...Most of the living things clinging to the rock were animals, many more animals than algae. The attached animals took fantastic plantlike shapes or spread, formless, across the rocks. Sharing the space were more everyday creatures—crabs, snails and fishes."

"A patchwork of colors and textures ...

...covered the rocks. To my left, a field of tiny strawberry anemones spread over an outcropping. Ahead, pink and purple hydrocorals grew on a rock face, like a small stony forest. And all around, crusts of sponges and tunicates were bordered by bright orange cup corals and bushy colonies of bryozoans."

—notes from a kelp forest dive

California hydrocoral
Stylaster californicus

Blue-banded goby
Lythrypnus dalli

Orange cup coral
Balanophyllia elegans

Red volcano sponge
Acarnus erithacus

Orange puffball
Tethya aurantia

Strawberry anemone
Corynactis californica

Sharp-nosed crab
Scyra acutifrons

Cup coral
Astrangia lajollaensis

In the water column

"Gliding among columns of kelp ...

... I swam through clouds of fishes, passing between thick stands and open sunlit 'meadows.' Fishes darted in and out of sight, more kinds than I've seen anywhere else along this coast. When I brushed a kelp frond, I saw part of it glide away—it was a giant kelpfish, camouflaged so well I hadn't even seen it! As I watched a kelp rockfish hanging in the water, hypnotized, a swarm of golden señoritas flew by."

—notes from a kelp forest dive

Kelp surfperch
Brachyistius frenatus

Giant kelpfish
Heterostichus rostratus

Señorita
Oxyjulis californica

Giant kelp
Macrocystis pyrifera

Kelp rockfish
Sebastes atrovirens

Blacksmith
Chromis punctipinnis

◀ *Pacific sardines*

In the kelp forest

"There was a billowing something on a strand of kelp ...

... so I stopped for a closer look; it was a sea slug—a Melibe. It cast its huge hood through the water, netting tiny crustaceans. The hood contracted and the sea slug swallowed its catch. When a prowling kelp crab approached, the Melibe dropped off the plant, turned upside down, and swam away."

"I wanted to go back and explore those corners again ...

... but when I glanced at my pressure gauge I realized I was running out of air. Catching my partner's attention, I gave the 'low on air—going up' sign. We slowly ascended and, after rejoining the surface, began the long kick back to shore."

—notes from a kelp forest dive

Kelp crab
Pugettia richii

Melibe
Melibe leonina

The Kelp Forest

Cabezon
Scorpaenichthys marmoratus

"Cabezon" means "large head" in Spanish, and this sculpin can gulp some good-sized prey. Cabezon can swallow whole abalones, regurgitating the inedible shells.

diet: crustaceans, fishes, molluscs
size: to 2.5 ft. (76 cm)

Giant sea cucumber
Parastichopus californicus

The sea cucumber just lopes along placidly. But if it meets a hungry sea star, the slowpoke breaks out into a gallop.

diet: organic particles
size: to 10 in. (25 cm)

Red abalone
Haliotis rufescens

This big marine snail is a gourmet item for many species, including sea otters, octopuses, fishes and people. But the abalone's strong suction foot and thick shell make them all work for their treat.

How old is the abalone you've found? Hard to tell. Abalone grow about an inch per year for the first five years, then slow way down. It could take a red abalone twenty to thirty years to reach nine inches.

diet: red and brown algae
size: to 1 ft. (30 cm)

China rockfish
Sebastes nebulosus

Don't judge this fish by its yellow streak. A territorial type, the China rockfish will readily chase trespassers off its piece of the rocky reef.

diet: invertebrates, fishes
size: to 17 in. (43 cm)

Tubesnout
Aulorhynchus flavidus

In spawning season, the male tubesnout builds a nest in the kelp, weaving fronds together with a sticky thread, spider fashion. After several females lay eggs there, he guards them till they hatch.

diet: zooplankton, larvae
size: to 7 in. (18 cm)

Blacksmith
Chromis punctipinnis

Although these fish are called "blacksmiths," most are really in the cleaning business. Adult blacksmiths pick parasites off other pest-ridden fishes.

diet: plankton, crustaceans, parasites
size: to 1 ft. (30 cm)

Sea lettuce
Ulva sp.

Although thin and fragile-looking, sea lettuce takes a lot of abuse—pounding waves and drying sun. These plants are "weeds": they quickly over-grow barren areas.

Coralline sculpin
Artedius corallinus

Masters of camouflage, these sculpins match the background so perfectly you won't find one till it moves. This tricky fish stays near coralline algae, concealed from both predators and prey.

diet: small invertebrates
size: to 5.5 in. (14 cm)

California hydrocoral
Stylaster californicus

This rock-tree houses a colony of tiny anemonelike animals. The colony acts as a unit, with each member specializing in one task—feeding, defense or reproduction—for the benefit of all.

diet: microscopic zooplankton
size: to 1 ft. (30 cm)

Painted greenling
Oxylebius pictus

Dark bars mark the greenling, alias "convictfish." In summer the male is known to turn almost black. Lying low by his rocky hideout, he lures a female in, to lay eggs. Though he guards them fiercely, he eats a few, too.

diet: shrimp, fish eggs
size: to 7 in. (18 cm)

Mimicking crab
Mimulus foliatus

This colorful crab eats giant kelp, making its home in the rootlike holdfast. In a kelp forest near here, biologists found 73 of these crabs crammed into a single square yard of holdfast.

diet: kelp
size: to 3 in. (8 cm)

Fish-eating anemone
Urticina piscivora

While more delicate species only rake in bits of food, this anemone has sturdy tentacles that bring down big game like shrimps and small fishes.

diet: invertebrates, small fishes
size: to 8 in. (20 cm)

Strawberry anemone
Corynactis californica

This animal multiplies by dividing in two. These two divide, too, and the clones keep splitting till they cover a square yard or more.

diet: copepods, larvae, zooplankton
size: to 1 in. (2.5 cm)

Burrowing anemone
Pachycerianthus fimbriatus

The tentacles are just the tip of the anemone; the tube is two feet long. Besides anchoring and protecting the delicate animal in the shifting sand, the tube shelters the anemone when it withdraws from its enemies.

diet: small invertebrates
size: to 14 in. (35 cm)

Blue-banded goby
Lythrypnus dalli

This bright little slip of a fish sits just outside its hole, protecting its property. A goby's not much of a fighter, though—when trouble comes, it runs.

diet: small crustaceans
size: to 2.5 in. (6.5 cm)

Brown rockfish
Sebastes auriculatus

Biologists discovered these rockfish have a homing instinct. Fish caught, tagged and released two miles away were later found back at their original home.

diet: crustaceans, small fishes
size: to 21.5 in. (55 cm)

Red volcano sponge
Acarnus erithacus

With no gut, no mouth, no muscles, nerves or organs, the sponge is a pretty simple animal. This group of cells does manage to take in water and strain it for food, spurting the rest out the "volcanos" you see.

diet: bacteria, organic particles
size: to 3.5 in. (9 cm)

Kelp bass
Paralabrax clathratus

Usually loners, kelp bass join together to prey on small schooling fishes. They attack the school from all angles and may leap out of the water in hot pursuit.

diet: small fishes, squid, crustaceans
size: to 28.5 in. (72 cm)

Orange puffball
Tethya aurantia

Though it's a simple animal, high powers of healing and regeneration are within this sponge's sphere. When parts become infected, the puffball isolates and sheds them.

diet: bacteria, organic particles
size: to 3 in. (8 cm)

Giant kelpfish
Heterostichus rostratus

Odds are you won't find this cleverly camouflaged fish. It looks like a blade of kelp that has two round eyes.

diet: small crustaceans, fishes, molluscs
size: to 2 ft. (61 cm)

In the bay and beyond, these artful dodgers amaze us

Common cuttlefish
Sepia officinalis

Flashing bright, a swarm of sleek squid speeds through the open sea. On rocky floors far below, an octopus prowls, changing to look like rock, then weeds, then rock again, as it goes. And half a world away, a chambered nautilus hovers above the slopes of a deep, dark reef.

As awful as man thought them, now we know them to be awesome. Changing color, slipping away, baffling predators, outwitting prey—these boneless creatures perform feats their clam cousins couldn't dream of. And long before sharks, they ruled the seas.

Octopus and kin: quick and keen, these active hunters live lives of magic—and mystery

Long, long ago, nautiluses ruled the seas

Chambered nautilus
Nautilus sp.

A snail-like animal gave rise to nautiluses, octopuses and squids. This cephalopod class appeared five hundred million years ago, long before fishes.

Slowly, the cephalopods' protective shells changed into something like the Goodyear blimp. Gases in the chambers of the shell raised these animals clear of the bottom.

Once off the ground, cephalopods needed a means of travel, so they developed a water-jet system. And some freewheelers shifted from a bulky outer shell to a more compact inner one.

When fishes began to flourish, the cephalopods declined. No one knows exactly why. Today nautiluses, octopuses and squids are all that remain of this once-great ruling class.

▼ **Giant octopus**
Octopus dofleini

Octopus and Kin

These active hunters are bags of tricks

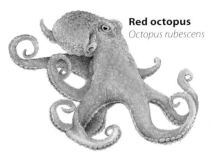

Red octopus
Octopus rubescens

How do octopus suckers work?

To grab a crab, an octopus draws up the centers of its suckers to create a vacuum. Octopuses have tremendous gripping power. It takes a forty-pound pull to release the grip of a three-pound octopus.

An octopus keeps pace on eight

On its eight legs and thousands of suckers, an octopus creeps, crawls and glides over the ocean floor. To escape danger, the octopus sucks in water and expels it through a siphon, whooshing away.

Squid are seagoing jetsetters

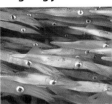

Squids squirt water through their siphons to jet through the open seas. Fins along their sides act like the wings of jets, steadying them as they go. Using siphon and fins, one kind of squid takes short flights.

Reach out and touch and taste someone

An octopus explores with its tentacles and suckers. The suckers can taste the difference between sweet, sour and bitter, and can feel if something's rough or smooth. But an octopus can't tell the size or shape of an object just by touching.

The eyes have it: an octopus goes for motion

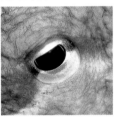

To see something passing by its hole, an octopus raises its eyes like periscopes, watching through its alien-looking rectangular pupils. An octopus's eyes work somewhat like ours. So far as we know, it can recognize shapes like squares and circles, and can tell the size and distance of objects.

Squids have orgies, but octopuses have close encounters

Unlike the frenzied free-for-all of spawning squid, octopuses have more intimate encounters. Because an octopus sees most anything that moves as food, the male must signal the female that he's a mate, not a meal. Some males flash colors or stripes, others curl back their tentacles to show suckers.

Call its bluff, and the octopus vanishes

When a threatened octopus can't hide, it tries to scare off the enemy by bristling its skin, puffing up or raising its tentacles. If that doesn't work, it shoots a blob of dark ink. While the enemy grabs at the phantom octopus, the real one jets away, melting into the background.

How does an octopus change color?

Elastic bags of color, or chromatophores, cover the body of an octopus. They hold yellow, red, orange, blue or black pigments. When the tiny muscles around them contract, the colors show as large spots; when they relax, the colors shrink.

A change from red to white takes less than a second.

Octopuses change to match mood or location

What if you could change your shape or color at will? A red octopus can easily blend with sand, rocks and plants, or ripple with colors to match the changing light.

Red octopus make quick changes many times in a day. In less than a second, this octopus can bleach white. It can also stretch smooth and paper-thin or puff out with warts and bristles.

While stalking or pouncing on prey, an octopus often flushes red.

When engaging enemies, octopuses may flash dark or bright, then go pale.

If frightened, dark spots or stripes appear on an octopus's body to make it look larger.

Red octopus
Octopus rubescens

An octopus can change its pace

A two-spotted octopus spends most of the time hiding or searching for food on the bottom. Using its arms and suckers it can slowly creep or quickly crawl.

But if it's in danger, the octopus may jet away into open water.

Two blue, eyelike spots on the web just below the eyes give this octopus its name.

Two-spotted octopus
Octopus bimaculoides

Octopus and Kin

Does it look like a monster to you?

Giant octopus
Octopus dofleini

People once called it "devilfish"; they said it was ferocious, blood-thirsty and strong enough to sink ships. In fact, the giant octopus is shy and poses little danger to divers, fishermen or swimmers.

Octopuses hide by day and hunt by night

By day, when hungry fishes prowl, an octopus hides in its den: under rocks or in holes, bottles and other junk. But under the cover of twilight, an octopus turns hunter, stalking crabs, snails and fishes.

A pile of empty shells marks an octopus's garden

When a crab walks by, the octopus pounces, enveloping the prey. Holding on with suckers, it cracks the shell with its beak and injects poison. It then returns home to eat the meal. After finishing the last morsel, the octopus sets the shell in the "garden" outside its den.

This creature is a native of the tropical Pacific

Chambered nautilus
Nautilus sp.

This cousin of the octopus is a living link with the past—little has changed for over one hundred fifty million years. Its simple eyes may see no more than the difference between dark and light. The nautilus uses its more than ninety tentacles to touch and taste the world.

The nautilus rises eerily

To avoid predators by day, the nautilus lingers along deep reef slopes, some as deep as 2,000 feet. At night, it migrates to shallower waters and cruises the reefs, trailing several tentacles in search of food.

The nautilus builds this spiral shell, but always lives in the last chamber. The other chambers contain gas or liquid, which this animal uses to control its buoyancy.

Fossil nautilus
Nautilus gabbi

A hundred million years ago, nautilus and their kind swam the seas of northern California. When the animals died on the seafloor, their shells filled with mud. As mud turned to stone the shells dissolved, leaving molds.

Fossils are our record of those ancient days. In 35,000,000 years, nautiluses dwindled from 2,500 species to four or five. But the nautiluses left us a living fossil, too.

Ammonite

Ammonites are relatives of the octopuses. Their fossilized shell is said to resemble the horn of a ram. Ammonites lived 135 to 400 million years ago and are now extinct.

Ammonites were named after the ancient Egyptian god Ammon, who was represented as a ram's head.

CUTTLEFISH AREN'T COMMON HERE

Common cuttlefish
Sepia officinalis

Cuttlefish are armed to hunt. When a shrimp or fish is in range, the cuttlefish aims—and shoots out two tentacles to seize its prey. Like their octopus kin, cuttlefish hide from enemies with color-change and clouds of ink.

Cuttlefish don't live in Monterey Bay; they're native to the Mediterranean and Eastern Atlantic.

Cuttlefish hatch from a "grapevine"

Cuttlefish lay their eggs in bunches, each grapelike egg encased in inky jelly. The aquarium has raised several generations from egg bunches.

▲ *Common cuttlefish*

▲ *Cuttlefish mating*

The Deep Reefs

*Eighty million years ago the earth
shuddered and shook; up from the
basement pushed granite reefs
to tower over the rocky floor.*

There's a constant dark feast
on the rich, cold deep reefs

Today the deep reefs loom over a sandy plain in the cold, dark, quiet waters a hundred to four hundred feet deep. The reefs are covered in living color—a turf that seems to be made of mosses and fabulous flowers.

Look again: these are animals carpeting the rock. They flourish in this sunless sea, conquering a realm where few plants could survive.

Lurking in caves, hiding in shadows, large wolf-eels and lingcod wait for prey to stray too near. Warily, sculpins hug the rubble, their mottled bodies blending with the floor. Clouds of rockfishes float by the reef, ready to vanish between rocks when larger predators arrive.

The deep reefs: a bountiful haven for those who elude their hunters.

China rockfish
Sebastes nebulosus

◄ *Colorful rockfishes
fade to gray in the dim
light of the reef.*

Strange creatures spend dark days hunting and hiding

Sunflower star
Pycnopodia helianthoides

Biggest star on the coast, this "twenty-arm star" starts with five arms and adds more as it grows. Known also for its big appetite, an oncoming star makes creatures flee.

diet: sea urchins, clams, snails, crabs
size: to 40 in. (1 m)

Wolf-eel
Anarrhichthys ocellatus

This night prowler leaves its den for dinner

Hardly a wolf, not really an eel, this fierce-looking fish spends the day quietly in a cave, wriggling out at night to feed.

Though some divers say the wolf-eel can bite a broomstick in half, this predator deserves a better reputation. Wolf-eels chomp on crabs, mussels and urchins; they don't eat divers or their brooms.

Lingcod
Ophiodon elongatus

Lingcod have huge appetites . . . and the jaws to match

You might guess the big mouth means this fish is a predator; if you look at their fins you'll get another clue to the lingcod's lifestyle.

Rather than chase after prey, a lingcod lies in wait. Broad pectoral fins help it balance on the seafloor till it's time to pounce.

They usually ambush other fishes, but lingcod will eat anything they can sink their teeth into—including younger lingcod.

Which jaws could crush a crab?

Look at the teeth on these two former fishes: One has massive grinding molars, while the other has teeth that are quite sharp. What kinds of foods were these teeth designed to eat?

Lingcod teeth have their strong points; they're efficient for piercing wiggly fishes. In fact, the lingcod is the most important fish predator on the deep reefs. But…

…when it comes to crushing hard-shelled crabs, mussels and sea urchins, the strong jaws and heavy teeth of the wolf-eel were made to grind away for years.

White-plumed anemone
Metridium giganteum

BOTTOM DWELLERS

Why do these rocks look alive?

Sculpins and other bottom-living fishes often look like the rocks they rest on. This camouflage works—as long as they sit still. If you look closely, you'll notice some have triangular bodies. That stable shape helps the fishes maintain their rock act.

Blackeye goby
Coryphopterus nicholsii

This goby grips the bottom with pelvic fins that have fused into a suction cup. Gobies are territorial; they stick close to home.

diet: small invertebrates
size: to 6 in. (15 cm)

Grunt sculpin
Rhamphocottus richardsonii

This comical little fish takes short hops across the floor, or walks on its long red fins. Even stranger is the way this sculpin got its name: take it from the water, and it grunts.

diet: crustaceans
size: to 3 in. (8 cm)

Sailfin sculpin
Nautichthys oculofasciatus

Would you believe this fish's long "sail" fin helps it hide? Instead of attracting attention, that rippling fin blends in with the algae-covered rocks.

diet: small crustaceans
size: to 7 in. (18 cm)

CREVICE DWELLERS

All-night diners feed on the rocky reefs

What's behind the whiskers? The business end of a sea cucumber, tucked in with its bushy tentacles out to catch food. Any antennae you see belong to shrimps; they run out for a bite, but retreat when a fish swims by. Such creatures hide because they lack other defenses.

Spot prawn
Pandalus platyceros

This shrimp has a big problem: it's one of the reef fishes' favorite foods. Though it hides 700 feet deep in rocky canyons, the prawn also falls prey to the commercial fisher-men of Monterey Bay.

diet: organic particles
size: to 5.5 in. (14 cm)

Quillback rockfish
Sebastes maliger

Tiger rockfish
Sebastes nigrocinctus

The Deep Reefs

Where can a bright red fish hide?

Look at these fishes in a different light

Because they live too deep for red light to reach them, these bright red rockfishes look black or gray. Here you can see how their predators or prey might miss them: they merge with dark shadows on the reef.

While all our local rockfishes are part of the same big family, sixty species strong, not all wear warm, brilliant colors. As a rule, the rockfishes that live in cool-hued kelp forests or in shallows are drab green and brown.

They play predator and prey in a hungry mob scene

Crowds of rockfishes cluster just above the reefs. If a hungry fish or seal comes by, the rockfishes duck between the boulders. But most of the time, they just hang there, snacking on the smaller fishes, octopuses and shrimps on the rocks, until ocean currents bring in another movable feast.

Fish-eating anemone
Urticina piscivora

While more delicate species only rake in bits of food, this anemone has sturdy tentacles that bring down big game like shrimps and small fishes.

diet: invertebrates, small fishes
size: to 8 in. (20 cm)

Rosy rockfish
Sebastes rosaceus

Think a purple-spotted red fish would attract some attention? Not in the deep reefs. Since they're too deep for red light to reach, a red fish looks gray, blending with the shadows.

diet: small fishes, crustaceans
size: to 11 in. (28 cm)

Sink or swim?

Why don't fish sink?

Are you watching a rockfish that's hovering? Floating close to a crevice? Just resting? Wherever your fish is, it's using a buoyancy-regulating organ called a swimbladder to stay in place.

To rest, a fish must be as dense as water. More dense, and it sinks; less dense, and it goes up and away.

A gas-filled swimbladder makes the heavy fish lighter. As the fish swims up or down, it controls the amount of gas in the sac so it can hover at any level.

Deep reef fishes live under lots of pressure

These fishes usually live more than a hundred feet deep, where the pressure is much greater than at the surface. Thanks to their swimbladders, they've adjusted to the relative lack of pressure here.

The deep reefs

Take a closer look at the animals that live in the deep reefs.

Common murre
Uria aalge

Like penguins, a murre flies through the water with the greatest ease. You may see this bird wing by, chasing fishes. Its silvery diving suit is made of air bubbles caught in its feathers.

diet: fishes
size: to 17 in. (43 cm)

Canary rockfish
Sebastes pinniger

To deceive prey, rockfish like the canary put on a great act. They hang motionless above rocky reefs, ready to snap up fishes that venture too close.

diet: fishes, krill
size: to 30 in. (76 cm)

Starry rockfish
Sebastes constellatus

While it's just as reddish and fond of rocks as every other reddish rockfish, this fish can, indeed, be distinguished. It's the only one wearing stars.

diet: invertebrates, small fishes
size: to 18 in. (46 cm)

Orange cup coral
Balanophyllia elegans

Corals in these cold waters don't build reefs like their tropical kin do. This coral does make its own outer skeleton: that cuplike limestone base underneath.

diet: small animals, organic particles
size: to 0.5 in. (1 cm)

Steelhead
Oncorhynchus mykiss

Once a rainbow trout leaves its stream to go to sea, it's called a "steelhead." After scattering widely in the sea for two or three years, they head unerringly back to their home streams, to spawn.

diet: shrimps, copepods, fishes
size: to 45 in. (1 m)

Bocaccio
Sebastes paucispinus

A bocaccio grows up fast, graduating from plankton-feeding to fish-eating in its first year. In summer, schools of young bocaccio take to the bay, snapping up fishes in the way.

diet: small fishes
size: to 3 ft. (91 cm)

Flag rockfish
Sebastes rubrivinctus

Young flags live near the ocean's surface, concealed beneath drifting kelp. As they age, they swim to deeper water and settle in among the rocks.

diet: small fishes, crustaceans
size: to 20 in. (51 cm)

Orange sea cucumber
Cucumaria miniata

Nestled between the rocks is the orange sea cucumber. Mucus on its showy tentacles traps food. In "finger-licking" fashion the cucumber sticks each tentacle in its mouth to get its meal.

diet: plankton, organic particles
size: to 10 in. (25 cm)

Red brotula
Brosmophycis marginata

Looking for a late-night diner? Watch for a long red fin waving in the rocks. This fish stays tucked in cracks by day, but after dark slips out to hunt for nightlife.

diet: small crustaceans, fishes
size: to 18 in. (46 cm)

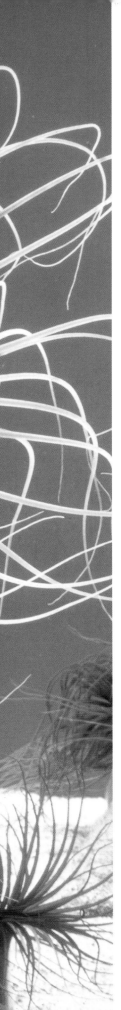

The Sandy Seafloor

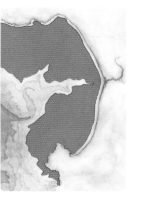

*In coarse sands near shore, currents push
miniature dunes across the floor, unsettling
everything. Plants can't anchor, but anemones
can, rooting tubes deep in the sand.*

These barrens are rich grounds for seeking buried treasures

Tough-skinned crabs scuttle across the shifting floor or dig in for protection. And flatfishes keep a low profile, concealed on the sand till they pounce.

But in muddy depths further out, the waves nearly cease. The bottom lies silent, cold and dark. Sand stars glide over the surface. Unearthly sea pens plant their bulbs and branch out; below them, thousands of tunneling worms are busy making a maze of the mud.

Up from the depths, in the light and open ocean, the scene changes to silver: a flurry of schooling fish flashes by, a shark sweeping after.

The sandy seafloor: where special breeds brave life in scouring sand—or choking mud— or wide open waters, the flatlands are alive with secret dramas.

Sand star
Astropecten armatus

◄ *The sandy seafloor has
a hidden treasure of life,
like these burrowing
anemones that anchor a
leathery tube two feet
beneath the sand.*

35

Above the Sandy Seafloor

Most marine fishes spend some time in schools

About three-quarters of all fishes spend their lives traveling in groups called schools. Fish in a school—sometimes thousands of individuals—act like cells of a single organism, darting and turning as one. To coordinate these maneuvers, each fish keeps an eye on its neighbor, using sight and pressure waves to determine its next move.

Besides swimming more easily in other fishes' slipstream, staying in schools helps fishes avoid predators and find food and mates.

Two-tone bodies help them vanish from sight

There's a reason why schooling fishes have bodies that are dark on top and silvery underneath. This countershading helps hide the fish from its predators or prey. Anyone looking up at the school might miss the silver bellies against the light sea surface; anyone looking down would view dark backs that disappear into the shadows below.

Jackmackerel
Trachurus symmetricus

BRITTLE STARS

Waving arms point out the home of the stars

Those aren't worms, they're brittle stars, sea star cousins that bury themselves up to the arms. They sink their disclike bodies for protection, leaving an arm or two free to wave in the water. At night, they stretch out to catch food particles, passing the bits down to the central mouth.

Sometimes a brittle star's wave hails a hungry fish. Fortunately, a star can't be tugged out by the arm. The arm snaps off, and a new one grows from the stump.

DIGGERS AND HIKERS

To cope with the open, seafloor creatures dig in or move on

Globe crab
Randallia ornata

You may see only the northern half of the globe crab, tucked into the seabed. If hiding doesn't fool its predators, the crab can flee: scuttling this way, then that, to lead its pursuer on a merry chase.

diet: invertebrates, dead organic matter
size: to 2 in. (5 cm)

CRABS

Armored crabs trek across the sandy plains

Crabs solve the seafloor housing shortage by carrying homes on their backs: hard outer skeletons that protect them from predators. But they pay a price for their lifetime supply of armor: they must molt, or shed the skeleton, in order to grow.

A hermit crab puts up a tough front, too, but its hind part is soft enough to curl into a secondhand snail shell. A growing hermit crab seeks progressively larger mobile homes.

FLATFISHES

These flatfish blend with any background

Sanddab
Citharichthys sp.

Most flatfishes are right-eyed, but the sanddab views the world left-side-up. How can you tell which is which-sided? Find where the fish's mouth is, relative to the eyes.

diet: worms, shrimps, squids, fishes
size: to 16 in. (41 cm)

On a sandy seafloor bare, I saw a fish that wasn't there

A flatfish lies low, keeping both eyes on the world

Shuffling into the sand, flatfishes cover themselves, often until only their eyes protrude. Both predators and prey (not to mention aquarium visitors) overlook these masters of camouflage. Their platelike bodies are flattened from side to side, rather than top to bottom, as in rays. Thus, flatfishes spend their lives lying on their sides.

Flatfishes are quick-change artists

Another part of their disappearing act is color change. More convincing than a chameleon, a flatfish can match its spots and splotches to the pattern of its surroundings. Like many other fishes, they also display countershading—dark coloration on top to blend with the seafloor, and white underneath, so when they swim up they can't be seen against the sunlit ocean surface.

FLATFISHES

Search the sand for hidden fishes

Diamond turbot
Hypsopsetta guttulata

This fish's small mouth hints at its feeding habits. Its big-mouthed relatives catch and eat other fishes, but the diamond turbot's small mouth is fit only for small morsels.

diet: worms, shrimps, clam parts
size: to 15 in. (38 cm)

Big skate
Raja binoculata

Skates propel themselves in two ways: kicking their pelvic fins to travel across the seafloor, or rippling their wings to glide through the water.

diet: crustaceans, fishes
size: to 8 ft. (2.4 m)

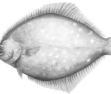

Longspine combfish
Zaniolepis latipinnis

This fish lives so deep we know little about its habits. Combfish do behave strangely if pulled up in a fishing trawl: once on deck, they bend like horseshoes and lie as if in a trance.

diet: small crustaceans
size: to 12 in. (30 cm)

Sand star
Astropecten armatus

The sand star can glide under the sand's surface as well as above it. If there's a supply of snails in the vicinity, the star glides a little faster.

diet: snails
size: to 10 in. (25 cm)

SAND DOLLAR

Sand dollar
Dendraster excentricus

Beachcombers know the skeleton, but few have seen the living sand dollar

In quiet waters, these flattened animals stand on end, half-buried in the sand. Where waters are rough, sand dollars hold their ground by lying flat—or burrowing under. Adults also fight the currents by growing heavier skeletons. The youngsters swallow heavy sand grains to weigh themselves down.

Sand dollars gamble on survival

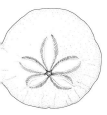

Since sand dollars don't seem to get around much, they reproduce by spawning: releasing eggs and sperm into the water. A female releases up to 380,000 eggs a year. The eggs float till fertilized by a nearby male, and currents carry the larvae as they develop. To survive, larvae must settle outside a sand dollar bed; those that drift inside would be eaten by adults.

These invertebrates take life with a grain of sand

Their velvety coat is really a series of spines and tube feet: a sand dollar's hunting gear. Club-tipped spines and sucker-tipped tube feet on its back trap food bits and algae, while thin spines underneath capture small prey. A sand dollar can trap food anywhere on its body, then pass it down food grooves to the mouth, swallowing lots of sand in the process.

BURROWING ANEMONE

Burrowing anemone
Pachycerianthus fimbriatus

Alarmed anemones go down the tubes

To shield itself from grit, this delicate creature makes a tough leathery tube, sinking it two feet deep into the sand.

When a predator like the barber slug comes by to clip off its tentacles, the anemone retreats quickly down the tube—sometimes pulling the slug in with it! Luckily, an anemone's tentacles can grow back after such attacks.

SEA PENS

A sea pen is made of thousands of individuals

Each tiny animal in a sea pen colony has a mouth and eight feathery tentacles. Groups of the animals work together: some feed and others pump water. This whole colony acts as one: if touched, the pen flashes light; if annoyed, the pen folds up and vanishes into the sand.

Sea pen
Ptilosarcus gurneyi

The Sandy Seafloor

THE SANDY SEAFLOOR

There are many different animals living in the sandy seafloor.

Leopard shark
Triakis semifasciata

Leopard sharks are often spotted in shallow water, where they nip off clam siphons and suck worms from the mud. Electroreceptors in their snouts help them home in on buried prey.

diet: crustaceans, fishes, worms, clams
size: to 6.5 ft. (2 m)

California halibut
Paralichthys californicus

The California halibut feeds on fishes and squids that can easily outswim it. To catch them, it lurks hidden in the sand, and lunges up to grab prey passing overhead.

diet: fishes, squids
size: to 5 ft. (1.5 m)

Sunflower star
Pycnopodia helianthoides

Biggest star on the coast, this "twenty-arm star" starts with five arms and adds more as it grows. Known also for its big appetite, an oncoming star makes creatures flee.

diet: sea urchins, clams, snails, crabs
size: to 40 in. (1 m)

Striped bass
Morone saxatilis

Like so many others in California, the striped bass came here from out-of-state. This East Coast native lives in both salt water and fresh, moving upriver to spawn.

diet: shrimps, fishes
size: to 32 in. (82 cm)

Sevengill shark
Notorynchus maculatus

That single dorsal fin marks the sevengill as a very primitive shark, little changed over the past hundred million years. The seven gill slits are also unusual: most sharks have just five.

diet: sharks, skates, rays, other fishes
size: to 8.5 ft. (2.6 m)

Black surfperch
Embiotoca jacksoni

A jack-of-all-trades, the black surfperch doesn't choose one lifestyle but lives in many different environments, eating everything from worms to other fishes' parasites.

diet: worms, bryozoans, crustaceans
size: to 14 in. (36 cm)

Sand-rose anemone
Urticina columbiana

It's too late for prey that chance upon this sand trap. Swallowing its food whole, the sea anemone digests the soft parts and spits out the rest.

diet: invertebrates, small fishes
size: to 10 in. (25 cm)

Giant sea bass
Stereolepis gigas

Rare in the bay and growing rare off Baja, this giant bass is no spring chicken of the sea. In another 70 years, this fish could outweigh a 500-lb. gorilla—and he, too, will eat anything he wants.

diet: sharks, other fishes, crabs, lobsters
size: to 7 ft. (2.1 m)

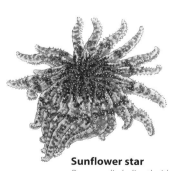

Sunflower star
Pycnopodia helianthoides

Pink sea star
Pisaster brevispinus

Bat ray
Myliobatis californica

This star's pretty pink wrap hides the inside story: it has a dramatic way of dealing with prey. Stretching tube feet down into sand till they hit a clam, the star can haul it up—or send its stomach down, to eat.

diet: clams, snails, sand dollars
size: to 12.5 in (32 cm)

Orange cup coral
Balanophyllia elegans

Corals in these cold waters don't build reefs like their tropical kin do. This coral does make its own outer skeleton: that cuplike limestone base underneath.

diet: small animals, organic particles
size: to 0.5 in. (1 cm)

The batlike wings that gave this ray its name also serve in the hunt. When it beats them on the seafloor, the ray unearths worms and clams to munch on.

diet: molluscs, worms, crustaceans
size: to 6 ft. (1.8 m)

White-plumed anemone
Metridium giganteum

The feathery halo on this animal isn't just for show. Some of the delicate tentacles sweep the water for food; others viciously sting neighboring anemones if they venture too near.

diet: microscopic plankton, particles
size: to 24 in. (61 cm)

King salmon
Oncorhynchus tshawytscha

Though they spend most of their lives at sea, salmon hatch in freshwater rivers, and must return there to spawn. They can find the way to their home streams from thousands of miles out in the ocean.

diet: fishes, squids, crustaceans
size: to 58 in. (1.5 m)

Spiny dogfish
Squalus acanthias

Double trouble awaits the fish that tangles with this shark; a toxic spine rides in front of each dorsal fin. Spiny dogfish run in schools, moving between shallow water and deep.

diet: small fishes, crustaceans
size: to 4 ft. (1.2 m)

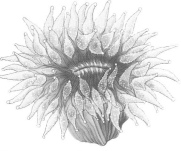

Brown cup coral
Paracyathus stearnsi

The Shale Reefs

Thirty million years ago, countless one-celled plants called diatoms rained down on the seabed, slowly piling over a thousand feet high. Time and pressure fused their glassy skeletons, transforming plants into solid rock.

Where clams dig the caves, all kinds of characters move in

Today, the flat-topped shale reefs are honeycombed with tunnels, all dug by mussels and clams that spend years boring into the rock. Some holes contain the clams at work; others, left vacant when clams die, conceal fishes and pliable types quick to move into a clam-made home.

Those who can cope with the seasonal sandstorms find the reef a great location. Clams snuggle in tunnels; peanut worms grow plump; and fringeheads guard their lodgings.

There's a million stories in the shale reef city.

Dig they must
Drillers make the most of a hard situation

◄ *Creatures crowd the shale reef, slipping through cracks or peeking tentacles out of crevices.*

43

Dig They Must

Would you believe there's a clam that can drill through solid rock?

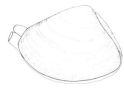

Called "boring clams" for their habit of tunneling into stone, they dig by steadily rocking their shells against shale. Date mussels dig in, too, but most of them use an acid.

After years of this boring activity, the hard-working mussel or clam gets its reward: a room of its own. Safe at last, the full-grown clam stops work, and gets ready to reproduce.

Their siphons are lifelines that bring the clams food and oxygen as they dig, and pass along sperm or eggs when they're done.

Here's a rare sight: reef creatures revealed

Suited for cave life, clams have siphons to connect them with the outside world. Siphons also keep them from burrowing trouble; when sand covers the clams, some stretch their siphons two feet high.

You can tell which are true drillers by checking their gear: tough shells with a cutting edge, to get them through the daily grind. The more delicate date mussels use acid to dig the rock; leathery "jackets" protect them. The others don't work at all—they drift in and grow in an old borer's home.

Shale's alive— with a bustling community

Sea lemon
Anisodoris nobilis

Bat star
Asterina miniata

The shale's population of fishes, chitons, worms and crustaceans uses the reef to hide from their hunters; many leave when they must go hunting, themselves. But the other rockbound clams, peanut worms and nestlers stay put, relying on their shelter for safety.

◄ *Wart-necked piddock*

Nestlers borrow burrows, then lead sheltered lives

The "swiss cheese" reef serves as an apartment house for more than a hundred animals besides the clams that dig the holes. Skinny fishes and tubular sea cucumbers fit right in, while brittle stars slip through the cracks.

What's hiding here?

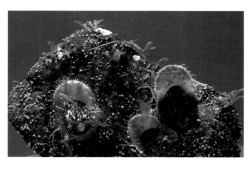

Shale's soft nature yields to drillers ... and opportunists move right in

Carnivorous chiton
Placiphorella velata

Would you fall prey to the hidden hunter?

Danger lurks where a peanut-sized chiton waits for even tinier prey. Holding its head-flag up like seaweed, the chiton looks like any other spot on the shale—till a worm crawls under, unaware. Slam! the trap snaps shut and the chiton dines.

Passersby are stunned when this shrimp pops off

Though some call them the "gunmen" of the sea, snapping shrimp don't shoot their prey— they stun them with percussion.

The shrimp stands guard outside its burrow, massive claw cocked. When a fish swims near and triggers the impulse to shoot, pop! The shock wave brings down the victim.

If a snapping shrimp loses its claw, the other one grows larger, to replace it.

What's that noise?

Under the Monterey wharf, you can hear the crackling "static" of thousands of snapping shrimp.

The sound puzzled scuba divers and submarine operators for years.

Snapping shrimp
Alpheus clamator

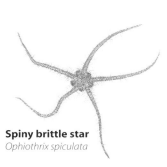

Spiny brittle star
Ophiothrix spiculata

Who hides in the shale?

In the shale reef, all kinds of animals find a place to fit in

Shale is full of homes and hiding places, from reef top to clam holes, from ledges to crevices. All kinds of animals move into these spaces, finding the shelter that fits them the best.

Shale rock is so soft, some animals can just dig right into it.

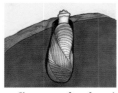

Clams are often found hiding in the shale rock. A clam with its rough, tough shell digs into the shale; its tubelike siphon keeps it linked to the outside world.

A rosy rockfish lurks under ledges, and hides where it's dark by day (but it sometimes comes out to hunt).

With most of its body tucked into a crack, a brittle star's thin body and flexible arms help it slip in and out of narrow places. It can stick out its free arms to feed.

A decorator crab lives on the reef top, where its dressed-up body makes it hard to see. This crab decorates its body with plants and animals so it blends in.

An abalone can tuck into a deep crevice, where otters can't reach it. An abalone can survive for more than 20 years in a safe crevice.

A peanut worm lives in places where it can snuggle in tight. Once a peanut worm moves into a clam hole, it stays put.

Yellowtail rockfish
Sebastes flavidus

No one ever thought rockfishes kept to one site; they were thought to always roam. Now it's been found that yellowtails can go home again—returning after being moved fourteen miles away.

diet: pelagic crustaceans, fishes
size: to 26 in. (66 cm)

Jackmackerel
Trachurus symmetricus

Notice the stripe that runs along this schooling fish's side. It marks the "lateral line," a sensory system fishes use to detect vibrations around them.

diet: plankton, lanternfishes, squids
size: to 28 in. (71 cm)

Cabezon
Scorpaenichthys marmoratus

"Cabezon" means "large head" in Spanish, and this sculpin can gulp some good-sized prey. Cabezon can swallow whole abalones, regurgitating the inedible shells.

diet: crustaceans, fishes, molluscs
size: to 2.5 ft. (76 cm)

Ocean whitefish
Caulolatilus princeps

These fish are the pioneers of their family. Most of the whitefish's relatives live in the tropics, but this species emigrated long ago to cold California waters.

diet: small fishes, squid, crustaceans
size: to 40 in. (1 m)

Yellowtail
Seriola dorsalis

Yellowtails flash through the water in large schools. With that streamlined shape, they're fast enough to catch squids and quick silvery little anchovies.

diet: fishes, squids, crabs
size: to 5 ft. (1.5 m)

Vermilion rockfish
Sebastes miniatus

Looking for a familiar face? You may have already met this one, as "red snapper"; if you fish, you may call it "rockcod." Allow us to re-introduce you: this fish is really a rockfish, and neither a snapper nor cod.

diet: fishes, crustaceans, squids
size: to 2.5 ft. (76 cm)

White sturgeon
Acipenser transmontanus

This primitive fish moves easily from salt water to fresh, leaving the sea for the rivers and streams where it spawns. Sturgeon grow slowly; one reached the ripe old age of 71.

diet: worms, crustaceans, clams, fishes
size: to 20 ft. (6 m)

Decorator crab
Loxorhynchus crispatus

To keep from becoming fish dinner, decorator crabs use camouflage. The young cover their shells with seaweed and other debris, costuming themselves to resemble long-legged rocks.

diet: algae, sponges, small crustaceans
size: to 4 in. (10 cm)

Rosy rockfish
Sebastes rosaceus

The Wharf

From the deep reefs to rocky shores, each part of Monterey Bay is distinct, its character molded both by physical factors and by the plants and animals living there.

Pier pressure is heavy where animals compete for space

Waves lapped the protected cove for eons. Then came the people, to build harbor and wharf. For all the time folks spent on the wharf, few knew the tides were washing tiny settlers by the pilings: invertebrate larvae seeking something to cling to, so they could attach and grow.

Today the pilings still seem a perfect place to settle: few plants grow under the shady pier, so there's more room for animals. The water is calm, and food comes in on the tide—or from above, when fishermen dump scraps from a catch.

But newcomers discover that animals already cover most every inch. Barnacles rule at the top; mussels cluster just below, and forty-year-old anemones stand their ground, ready to sting intruders. Up from the seafloor creep sea stars, stalking the unfortunates that settle too low.

The wharf: where creatures struggle for space, each specially armed for battle.

Pile surfperch
Damalichthys vacca

◄ *Beneath the waves, you'll find old wharf pilings thickly encrusted with anemones, barnacles, tunicates, and other marine life.*

49

Pilings support zoned neighborhoods

To survive, animals have to live within their limits

The plants and animals that crowd onto wharf pilings arrange themselves in zones from top to bottom. A creature's ability to withstand waves and drying, and to stand off enemies and competitors, combine to set its upper and lower limits.

Sea stars eat mussels up as far as they can reach

Mussels could live lower on the pilings than they do except for one problem: ochre sea stars favor mussels on the half-shell. These predators keep the lower pilings free of mussels. But since sea stars eat under water and their dining takes time, mussels that live higher between the tidemarks escape such unwanted attentions.

Which one wins when two mussels wrestle?

Strong anchoring threads help the heavyweight California mussel hang on in rough water, but in calm water, they are pinned down. Meanwhile, the weaker bay mussel snaps its thin threads and crawls to the edge of the clump, so it can feed and breathe easy.

Black surfperch
Embiotoca jacksoni

A jack-of-all-trades, the black surfperch doesn't choose one lifestyle but lives in many different environments, eating everything from worms to other fishes' parasites.

diet: worms, bryozoans, crustaceans
size: to 14 in. (36 cm)

Ochre star
Pisaster ochraceus

An ochre star can live without food for more than a year. During a long period of starvation, its arms will get shorter.

diet: mussels, barnacles, snails, limpets
size: to 22 in. (56 cm)

Giant acorn barnacle
Balanus nubilus

Under the volcano-shaped shell, a barnacle lies on its back and waits. When water rushes by, the barnacle stretches its feathery legs and kicks food down to its mouth.

diet: organic particles, plankton
size: to 4.5 in. (11 cm)

White surfperch
Phanerodon furcatus

Most marine fishes lay eggs, but surfperches, like mammals, give birth to living young. The young are quite mature at birth; newborn males can often mate immediately.

diet: clams, crustaceans
size: to 12.5 in. (32 cm)

Vermilion rockfish
Sebastes miniatus

Looking for a familiar face? You may have already met this one, as "red snapper"; if you fish, you may call it "rockcod." Allow us to re-introduce you: this fish is really a rockfish, and neither a snapper nor cod.

diet: fishes, crustaceans, squids
size: to 2.5 ft. (76 cm)

Pile surfperch
Damalichthys vacca

Rocks and wharf pilings provide shelter for both this fish and its prey. The fish eats crabs, mussels and snails, crunching them with strong teeth and swallowing, shells and all.

diet: mussels, chitons, crabs
size: to 17.5 in. (44 cm)

White-spotted anemone
Urticina lofotensis

Once thought to be a flower, this anemone is a predator. It stings and paralyzes the hapless crabs, fishes and others that stray near its venomous tentacles.

diet: invertebrates, small fishes
size: to 6 in. (15 cm)

Juvenile vermilion rockfish
Sebastes miniatus

You won't recognize these fish in six months when they're grown. Like the violet young rockfish that grow up blue, these red-and-gray juveniles turn vermilion as they mature.

diet: invertebrates, small fishes
size: getting bigger

Wharf community

One man's junk is anemone shelter

Like any good neighborhood, the wharf area has a housing shortage. But natural cracks and crannies aren't the only options for living space. Castoff junk provides hiding places for fishes and octopuses; barnacles and others attach themselves to the surfaces. Though these marine creatures are attracted to garbage, littering is still an ugly habit…so don't rush to the wharf to splash your trash.

Onespot fringehead
Neoclinus uninotatus

An old shoe, rusty can or bottle is a fringehead's dream home. Tucked snugly into the junk with just his head poking out, a male guards his castle, ready to charge at trespassers.

diet: invertebrates
size: to 9 in. (23 cm)

Sarcastic fringehead
Neoclinus blanchardi

Find the mottled brown fish with a big mouth and you've found the sarcastic fringehead. Protective of its bottle, boot or rubble home on the bottom, this fish isn't above nipping out to nip at a passing diver.

diet: invertebrates, small fishes
size: to 10 in. (25 cm)

Rubberlip surfperch
Rhacochilus toxotes

Life is boring in the wharf

Borers eat themselves out of house and home

While mussels and other creatures form a living crust on the surface of wharf pilings, another group bores away at the wood from the inside. Beating the competition for space this way are the gribbles—related to the sowbug—and shipworms, which are really a kind of clam.

In one year of boring activity, gribbles or shipworms can riddle an untreated piling till it looks like a honeycomb.

Though they're only digging in for food and shelter, the trouble with gribbles and shipworms is their tunneling, which causes extensive damage to wooden structures.

SURFPERCHES

They're all in the family

The surfperch family began along this coast. Over time, the original species evolved into twenty-three; twenty-one of them live nearby. Each catches different prey and so avoids interfering with its cousins' livelihoods.

They do share important family traits: notice the small mouth, used to pick at food. And unlike most marine fishes, all surfperches give birth to living young.

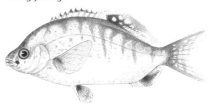

Rainbow surfperch
Hypsurus caryi

The Slough

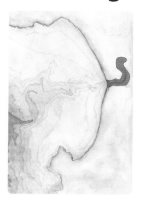

*Ancient rivers once flowed through
Elkhorn Valley, building mudflats and
marshes where they met the sea.*

Brimming with life,
the slough nourishes
all its creatures

The great rivers are gone now, but the marshes survive.

Visitors to the slough see a slow, quiet place: fog often muffles noises and softens outlines, and when the tide ebbs, the mud looks gray and barren. But those who learn to look find magic: bat rays glide through the channels, stopping to uncover a lunch of shrimp or worms; buried clams send up siphons like snorkels. And the graceful heron stands poised in the shallows, watching for unwary fishes.

◄ *This rich habitat is refuge
to many species of birds,
fishes and other animals.*
► ▲ *Great blue heron*
► *California sea lions*

55

Surveying the slough:
A channel-to-marsh transect

Follow the clues to discover the slough

Moon snail
Polinices sp.

The slough is full of fascinating stories and characters. Once you learn its language, you can read it like a book. A feather, an egg case, a trail through the mud can tell you what strange and wonderful creatures passed this way. Other signs tell tales of how the animals and plants here live their lives.

Come explore this setting of channel, eelgrass, mudflat and marsh, and discover its hidden nature.

Channels are the circulatory system of the marsh

Countless channels branch from the main tidal channel and snake through the marsh. They carry water to and from the higher ground,

feeding and flushing all sections of the marsh. These tidal creeks, some small enough to step across, are important rearing grounds for shiner surfperch and other fishes.

If you were a slough shrimp, clam or worm, which would you rather live in— murky water or clear water?

Murky, dirty water would best suit your taste. What looks like dirt is, to a slough dweller, a rich soup of one-celled plants, tiny animals and decayed matter. Living in this water, they are constantly surrounded by food.

Waving eelgrass beckons slough inhabitants

Eelgrass is one of the few marsh plants to grow under water in the slough. Like green palm oases in a mud desert, tufts of eelgrass attract a variety of creatures. They provide food and hiding places for invertebrates and fishes, root-stabilized mud for burrowers and mooring for herring eggs, hydroids and others.

Marsh plants cope with salt and soakings

Drenching tides and salty soil make life in the marsh impossible for all but a few types of plants. Pickleweed, the most successful plant in Elkhorn Slough, stores salt in its cells to combat the drying effects of sea water. Other plants store oxygen to carry them through when water drowns their roots.

They may look empty, but mudflats crawl with life

Dig up a shovelful of mud and you'll find clams, worms, crustaceans and other animals hidden beneath the surface. When the tide comes in they poke out heads and legs to feed. At ebb tide the small creatures retreat, as long-billed shorebirds move onto the flats to search them out.

Red phalarope
Phalaropus fulicaria

Unlike most birds, female phalaropes are brighter than males, but only during the breeding season. And while the females lead the courtship, males tend the nests and young.

diet: plankton, crustaceans, insects
size: to 9 in. (23 cm)

Red-necked phalarope
Phalaropes lobatus

To feed, a phalarope sits on the water and plucks tiny animals from the surface. Sometimes, the bird spins around in one spot to make a whirlpool. The whirlpool carries animals from below up to the surface where the bird can reach them.

diet: zooplankton
size: to 8 in. (20 cm)

THE SLOUGH

This shrimp's work is never done

This industrious creature keeps water flowing through its tunnels by beating the swimmerets on its tail. Like earthworms, ghost shrimp dine on the mud they dig. They eat a bucketful of earth every few weeks, absorbing the nutrients. Other animals take advantage of the shrimp's hard work: up to six species share these digs.

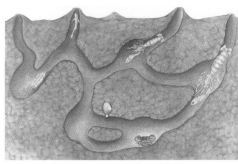

Ghost shrimp
Neotrypaea californiensis

Ghost shrimp colonies resemble a moonscape

A volcano-shaped mound erupts at each tunnel entrance, often spewing dirt as the shrimp works and covering neighbors, like the oysters. You'd be most likely to find traces of ghost shrimp at a slough's ocean end, where the sand-mud mix is right for building burrows.

Fat innkeeper worm
Urechis caupo

Innkeepers maintain fine lodgings for their buddies in the mud

Food, shelter and running water pumped by the innkeeper worm attract a motley crew of guests to this burrow. Some, like the arrow goby, check in and out quickly; others, like the pea crabs and scale worm, take up permanent residency. The innkeeper isn't bothered by these guests, but doesn't benefit, either.

Think a clam is a clam? Dig a little deeper

CLAMS

Clams do have differences: they all burrow, but long-necked ones like the geoduck sink lower than their short-necked kin. Heavy shells protect clams near the surface, while long, thin shells are best for quick digging. It's not even true that all clams are happy; if the cockle senses danger, it may vault violently from the mud.

Staying buried in mud is a soft life ...

... if you can eat, breathe and reproduce. Clams manage by sticking their necks out. Through the neck, or siphon, a clam sucks in food and water and sends out eggs or sperm. At ebb tide, clams pull in their siphons. If you visit a slough, look for telltale holes.

In the slough, the fishes come and go

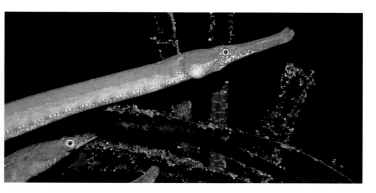

SLOUGH FISHES

Most fishes live in the slough part-time, shuttling from slough to sea. Sharks and others commute in to feed, while spawning herring come and go with the seasons. The permanent residents, like pipefishes, are left to cope with varying temperatures and salinity.

Pickleweed
Salicornia virginica

Pickleweed stores salt in its branches to fight the drying effects of sea water. Next time you're in the slough, take a taste of the plant's juicy stems to discover how it got its name.

size: to 2 ft. (61 cm)

Eelgrass
Zostera marina

Eelgrass is home to a variety of animals, including perfectly camouflaged pipefish that look like leaves with eyeballs. Other slough inhabitants, like worms and shrimps, burrow in the mud around its roots.

Shiner surfperch
Cymatogaster aggregata

A male shiner surfperch changes colors with the seasons. Come summer, he covers his shiny silver and yellow stripes with a darker suit of courtship colors.

diet: small crustaceans
size: to 5 in. (13 cm)

Bay pipefish
Syngnathus leptorhynchus

Like their curled-up cousin the seahorse, pipefish usually swim upright, beating their small fins. When this vertical fish feeds, it gets an inch away from its prey—and slurps.

diet: small crustaceans, larval fishes
size: to 13 in. (33 cm)

Dwarf surfperch
Micrometrus minimus

The scientific name for this fish means "little mother." It's an appropriate handle for the smallest of the surfperches, a family whose females bear live young.

diet: algae, small invertebrates
size: to 3.5 in. (9 cm)

Each sea hare is both male and female

Mating in chains and circles, bisexual sea hares may lay up to eighty million eggs apiece. Most of these mother-fathers' eggs are eaten by predators.

Sex in the slough ...

They're parents with/without partners

Obelia shifts from sexual to asexual reproduction. As an asexual colony, *Obelia* buds off jellyfish that swim away to spawn. The larvae that result start new colonies.

Sea hare
Aplysia californica

... how they multiply

Animals choose between quality and quantity

Most marine animals either send out clouds of eggs and sperm, leaving fertilization to chance, or they lay and then abandon thousands of eggs. But a few opt for quality over quantity. Surfperches, rays and some sharks give birth to live young. Though livebearers have fewer offspring than egglayers do, their young emerge large, well-equipped for survival.

Animals give birth when food is abundant and temperatures mild. Those with complex cycles must time it right. In December, male mudsuckers are challenging one another to mouthfights and scooping out nests for spawning. By starting so early, they ensure their young will be old enough by summer to survive the hot, salty days.

THE SLOUGH

The slough bursts with growing things

Nutrients from both land and sea flow into the marsh and fertilize its soil. The few plants hardy enough to stand the salinity and frequent flooding face little competition; they grow vigorously. Marshes produce more green per acre than prime farmland.

Plants contribute to the underwater economy

Marshes don't have cows, so what eats this abundance of plants? Nothing much—until the plants die and decay. The resulting muck is supper for animals that feed on the slough floor. These creatures are eaten in turn by birds and fishes, spreading the slough's bounty far afield.

A slough's community nursery serves many species

Besides feeding marsh dwellers, the slough nourishes their young. Many fishes lay their eggs here, or give birth to live broods. Others drift in from the ocean to spend a sheltered youth in shallow waters. The marsh also hides birds as they sit on their nests.

What good is a weedy old salt marsh?

Wildlife flocks to Elkhorn Slough

Marshes may not look appealing at first glance, but patient watchers discover an incomparable habitat here. Young sharks and English sole swim in the channels. Migrating birds use coastal marshes as crucial food and rest stops, and other birds live here full time. If you visit Elkhorn Slough, you may even see mud-lounging harbor seals, hauled out to bask.

Using marshes without using them up

Considered "wastelands" for many decades, California marshes were filled in, diked off or dredged out for human uses. Our remaining wetlands are a valuable, vulnerable resource, and must be used wisely.

If we tread lightly, the marshes will remain available to clamdiggers, fishermen, nature lovers, boaters, birders, biologists—and animals— for years to come.

THE SLOUGH

The Sandy Shore
(Aviary)

*From the water to its upland edges,
the slough conceals its inhabitants.*

The slough harbors a
wealth of hidden wildlife

Invisible rays and other fishes cruise the channels; clams and worms burrow and vanish; small mammals, like the muskrat, leave only tracks to mark their passage. And while visitors to the slough would easily see the snowy white egret, they might miss those birds that hide or stand motionless, camouflaged.

Long-billed curlew
Numenius americanus

◄ *Above the marshes and wave-swept shores, you'll find tens of thousands of birds passing through during their annual migration in the spring and fall seasons.*

Dunes

California poppy
Eschscholzia californica

Heavy roots help the perennial poppies hold their ground. New poppies get their start when winter rains wash away salt in the soil surrounding the seeds.

size: to 4 in. (10 cm)

Beach sagewort
Artemesia pycnocephala

This aromatic cousin of the sage hangs on to the edge of the bluffs. Sagewort is a favorite hideout for deer mice, who must avoid hawks by day and foxes and owls by night.

size: to 28 in. (71 cm)

Lizard tail
Eriophyllum staechadifolium

This fuzzy, silver-green bush springs into view when its clusters of bright yellow flowers are in bloom. As the flowers dry, their seeds are shot-put into the wind.

size: to 5 ft. (1.5 m)

Pioneer plants settle a harsh new land

The plants that pioneer this dry, salty land borrow tricks from desert plants. They coat themselves with wax or hairs to reduce water loss, or store moisture in juicy leaves and stems. Dune plants also grow low, to avoid the wind. These first settlers stabilize the soil and add humus, making the way easier for later comers.

How do the sands that make up dunes get there?

Some sand grains were scoured from seaside cliffs north of Monterey; others were worn from inland rocks by rivers, which wash them into the bay. Ocean currents carry these rivers of sand—some 300,000 cubic yards a year— south along the coast, and deposit it on Monterey beaches. Blown inland, the sand forms these dunes.

Who's using the dune as a nest?

The snowy plover nests directly on the sand; both eggs and parent plover are so well camouflaged they are seldom seen. As the number of undisturbed dunes in the Monterey Bay area has shrunk, these privacy-loving birds have grown scarce.

Western sandpiper
Calidris mauri

In their gray winter plumage, Western sandpipers blend with the sand. But when winter wanes their gray heads and back will turn cinnamon—a color more suitable for courting.

diet: crustaceans, other invertebrates
size: to 6.5 in. (16.5 cm)

Black-necked stilt
Himantopus mexicanus

The long red legs are proof the stilt was built for wading. As the birds strike out across the mud, they may keep walking and picking insects till they're feeding in water up to their bellies.

diet: insects, crustaceans
size: to 14 in. (36 cm)

Ruddy turnstone
Arenaria interpres

When it hunts, the turnstone leaves no stone unturned. Using its sturdy beak, the bird flips aside stones, seaweed and shells in its search for hidden dinner.

diet: invertebrates
size: to 9.25 in. (23.5 cm)

Willet
Catoptrophorus semipalmatus

Most shorebirds stick to one kind of hunting, but the willet finds its dinner in many places. The bird uses its sturdy beak to probe rocky tide pools, beaches, mudflats and grassy fields for food.

diet: crabs, worms, insects, snails
size: to 16 in. (41 cm)

Avocet
Recurvirostra americana

This wading bird's long bill curves up at the tip— a twist that enables it to scrape up food. As an avocet searches the mudflats and shallows, it sweeps the bill through the water like a scythe.

diet: crustaceans, other invertebrates
size: to 18 in. (46 cm)

THE SANDY SHORE

Beaches

Beach dwellers dig in against a rough-and-tumble life

Beach sand churns with each wave, but creatures that live here have learned to stay put, burrowing quickly if dislodged. Since there isn't much to eat in the sand, these invertebrates catch lunch as it comes in on the waves. As the waves go out, the burrowers become meals for shorebirds that probe the sand.

Waves

Waves sculpt the beaches with moving sand

Each wave that breaks along the shore wreaks minor havoc. It claws the beach and carries away the churned-up sand. Wave by wave, the ocean moves tons of sand south along the coast. Waves change the beaches' profiles from season to season, eating them away in winter and building them back in summer.

▲ *Black-necked stilt*

Fleshy jaumea
Jaumea carnosa

The fleshy parts store water to help jaumea battle salinity. Though it joins pickleweed and other salt-fighters in midmarsh, this plant halts where there's a chance it might be covered by the tide.

size: to 1 ft. (30 cm)

Beach strawberry
Fragaria chiloensis

This perennial reproduces by sending out runners that take root, developing new plants at a distance from the parents. An offshoot is that the system works to stabilize the sand.

Salt grass
Distichlis spicata

It's a rare plant that can live in salty soil without wilting. Salt grass takes the salt in, then sweats it out, leaving crystals on its blades for the rain to wash away.

size: to 1 ft. (30 cm)

Leopard shark
Triakis semifasciata

Leopard sharks are often spotted in shallow water, where they nip off clam siphons and suck worms from the mud. Electro-receptors in their snouts help them home in on buried prey.

diet: invertebrates, fishes, worms, clams
size: to 6.5 ft. (2 m)

The Sandy Shore (Aviary)

THE SANDY SHORE

Shovelnose guitarfish
Rhinobatos productus

Compressed from belly to back, guitarfish bodies are attuned to life on the sand. This most ancient ray has been playing it flat for over 100,000,000 years.

diet: worms, clams, crabs, bottomfishes
size: to 5.5 ft. (1.7 m)

Killdeer
Charadrius vociferus

If a predator looms too near a killdeer's nest, the bird launches into its "broken wing" charade: dragging itself off, one wing twisted against its back, to lure the predator away from its young.

diet: insects
size: to 10 in. (25 cm)

Topsmelt
Atherinops affinis

Called "topsmelt" for their habit of swimming up near the surface, these fish school near shore. Because they can tolerate extremes in salinity, they also live in salt ponds twice as salty as the sea.

diet: small crustaceans
size: to 14 in. (35.5 cm)

Barred surfperch
Amphistichus argenteus

This fish's color is keyed to its habitat. The bars blend with the churning sea and the light-and-shadow ripples on the sand of its surf-zone home.

diet: sand crabs
size: to 17 in. (43 cm)

Walleye surfperch
Hyperprosopon argenteum

Most fishes lay thousands of eggs, but walleyes bear only up to a dozen live young. Why so few? Well-developed at birth, young surfperches hold a survival edge over other fishes' tiny hatchlings.

diet: small crustaceans
size: to 1 ft. (30 cm)

White sea bass
Atractoscion nobilis

Like giant sea bass, white sea bass are rare around here. But the two aren't related, and there's little they share. Giants grow enormous; whites, merely large. The giants have spots; young whites have bars.

diet: squid, sardines, other fishes
size: to 5 ft. (1.5 m)

Dune ryegrass
Leymus mollis

This hardy grass grows on the dunes just above the beach. By anchoring the shifting sand and cutting the wind, it makes a place where other plants can grow more easily.

Long-billed curlew
Numenius americanus

Worm beware—this bird's bill can probe deep in the mud. With a bill longer than any other shorebird's, the curlew has access to food no other bird can reach.

diet: insects, worms, crustaceans
size: to 26 in. (66 cm)

Bat ray

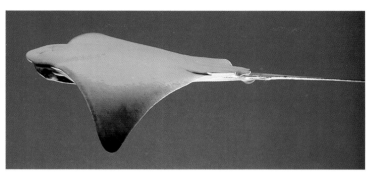

Bat ray
Myliobatis californica

Think of a ray as a flat, gentle shark

A bat ray may not look much like a shark, but they're cousins, akin under the skin. Both are boneless, their skeletons made of cartilage. And both have strong jaws and teeth, pectoral fins and gills. But a ray's flattened, its equipment rearranged to suit it for life on the bottom.

Why a bat?

Depending on your expert, they're called "bat" rays for their batlike flight ... or for their massive batlike heads, so you can argue about the common name, too. We do know their Latin name means "California grinder ray," after the way their teeth mash clams—and that's flat.

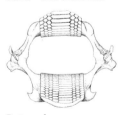

Bat ray jaws

Teeth like plates help rays crunch lunch

Bat rays fancy oysters and clams: heavy shelled shellfish that pointed shark teeth wouldn't put a dent in. To suit such food, a ray has flat plates for teeth, blunt crushers set well back in the mouth.

A ray's mouth is on the underside, but how does it keep from breathing in silt? Behind the eyes, there are two holes that open and close. A ray inhales through these spiracles, then exhales through the gills.

Bat rays don't shock and these won't sting

Many people misunderstand these placid creatures, but believe us: they're not electric rays, and won't lash out at you. Rays never attack, but they'll sting in self-defense, so watch out if you catch one while you're fishing.

Where is the sting?

We don't know how the story got started, but the stinging spine isn't at the tip of the tail—it's at the base, near the body.

Rays on exhibit have clipped spines and are used to people touching and feeding them.

Rays turn shark fins into wings

A ray's pectoral fins are big, broad wings joined to the head. Instead of swimming fish-style, tail flexing from side to side, a bat ray swims by flapping its wings.

Wings also work to dig up dinner. By beating them on the seabed, the ray unearths worms and clams.

They move to shallows to bear their broods

On the central California coast, bat rays wing into bays and tidal marshes like Elkhorn Slough in June and July. There, they bear their young: live offspring that emerge tail first, wings wrapped around the body.

To protect the mother, the newborn's stinging spine is rubbery and covered with a sheath. It soon hardens, and can be used for defense within days.

The Rocky Shore

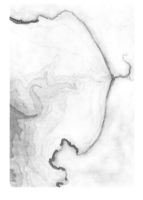

*At land's edge, the tide rushes in,
sweeping over the sea plants and animals
that embroider the shore.*

Life obeys the rule of the tides

The waves bring to life anemones that open like flowers, seaweeds that sway and barnacles that unfurl their feathery legs.

Delicate forms, they please the eye. But each is really a picture of grace under pressure. When the tide comes in, the struggle begins, as sea stars and fishes prowl for prey.

When the tide ebbs, the shore's exposed, life suspended high and dry. And storms roll in without warning, shocking the shoreline with tons of crashing water.

The rocky shore: where creatures contend with the challenge of life on the edge, they earn in return the sea's bounty.

THE ROCKY SHORE

◄ *Twice each day the
tide ebbs, unveiling a
cast of hundreds.*

The Rocky Shore

Living conditions change from zone to zone

Residents of the rocky shore survive where living conditions most closely suit their abilities and vulnerabilities.

In the highest zones, marine creatures must withstand long periods out of the water, where both temperature and salinity may reach extremes. Areas with crashing waves favor creatures that cling tightly. In lower zones, predators threaten, and competition crowds out many that would otherwise live there.

Dogwinkle
Nucella emarginata

Six-rayed star
Leptasterias hexactis

Ochre star
Pisaster ochraceus

Without water, intertidal animals would starve

Water is the waiter

Into the sunlit shallows flow nutrients for red, brown and green algae. Sea urchins, black turban snails, limpets and chitons munch and scrape the algae in turn. Also flooding the shore are tiny drifting animals and plants, or plankton. Barnacles filter out these tasty morsels, while shrimps and crabs dine on leftovers.

When the tide is in, the table is set

When the water's away, most intertidal animals hide in their shells, in crevices or under plants. Without water, there's no food to eat and no shield from the hot sun. But when the tide covers the plants and animals with water, the feast is on.

The water also brings danger

Sea slugs nibble sea anemones, octopuses pounce on passing crabs and snails, and dogwinkles drill through mussel and barnacle shells. Feeding time is short; soon the water withdraws. Nudibranches and octopuses seek shelter, sea anemones retract, snails clamp shut and crabs scurry off till the tide returns.

The Rocky Shore

There are three zones in the intertidal

High intertidal zone

Eroded periwinkle
Littorina keenae

Acorn barnacle
Balanus sp.

Rough limpet
Macclintockia scabra

Marine life adapts to living high and dry

Residents of the high intertidal zone have adapted to living out of water for all but a few hours each week. To keep from drying out, barnacles close their shells tight, limpets venture out only at night, and flatworms hide in the dampness under boulders. Animals here lie low during dry periods and burst into activity when the tide returns.

Mid-zone residents get the best and worst of two worlds

Creatures here face twin pressures: at low tide, they hide or clamp shut to keep moist. At high tide, they must avoid hungry sea stars and fishes and war with their neighbors for food and space. Each species meets these challenges with a unique blend of talents and tolerances. From barnacles atop the rocks to brittle stars beneath, they add to the diversity of this zone.

Middle intertidal zone

Green algae
Cladophora sp.

California mussel
Mytilus californianus

Surf grass
Phyllospadix scouleri

◀ At the middle intertidal zone, you'll find an array of seaweeds and animals each competing for a space on the rocks.

Low intertidal zone

Hopkins' rose
Hopkinsia rosacea

Abalone
Haliotis sp.

Red sponge
Acarnus erithacus

Down here, danger comes from neighbors

Inhabitants of the low zone don't need special ploys to stay wet, since they're rarely uncovered. The constant flooding subjects them to continuous predation and grazing. Predatory snails and sea stars push their prey into higher, safer zones while hungry grazers, such as the sea urchins, mow down seaweeds unlucky enough to settle within their reach.

Bat star
Asterina miniata

The Rocky Shore

In surge channels, it all comes and goes in the wash

As each wave comes and goes, water surges between the rocks like reversible rivers. It brings food and oxygen to the surge channel community and carries off its larvae and waste. Though channel residents avoid the crashing waves and drying sun overhead, they must struggle to stay put against rushing currents.

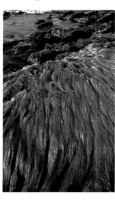

Surf grass
Phyllospadix scouleri

Underwater blossoms prove that surf grass isn't an alga. It's a flowering plant with true leaves, roots and seeds that lives in the sea.

size: to 3 ft. (91 cm)

Cabezon
Scorpaenichthys marmoratus

Cabezon crouch in cracks and under rocks to avoid the surge. Their broad pectoral fins and natural lack of buoyancy let them hold their ground on the seafloor.

diet: crustaceans, molluscs, small fishes
size: to 39 in. (99 cm)

Reef surfperch
Micrometrus aurora

Rather than hide or cling to the rocks, a surfperch in surge stays in the middle of the channel. The fish faces the current as it sweeps in and out, swimming to stay put.

diet: algae, invertebrates
size: to 7 in. (18 cm)

Leather chiton
Katharina tunicata

A chiton clings tightly with its muscular foot. Instead of a rigid shell, a chiton has eight overlapping plates. They make the animal flexible enough to hug bumpy surfaces.

diet: algae, diatoms
size: to 5 in. (12 cm)

Orange cup coral
Balanophyllia elegans

A cup coral larva crawls on the floor before settling. After cementing its limestone skeleton to a rock, the coral is set for life. Solitary corals, they take refuge in their "cups."

diet: small animals, organic particles
size: to 0.5 in. (1cm)

Purple sea urchin
Strongylocentrotus purpuratus

Wedged between rocks, holding on with hundreds of tube feet, sea urchins resist the surge. Each wave brings them bits of algae to eat.

diet: kelp, red algae
size: to 4 in. (10 cm)

Water brings life

Layers of interwoven mussel shells look lifeless on shore, but under water they come alive. The shells open slightly and tiny hairs, or cilia, beat rhythmically to draw in water carrying tiny particles of food. Inside, the gills filter the water and catch the food in mucus before it moves to the mouth.

To collect enough food to survive, a mussel filters two to three quarts of water an hour.

California mussel
Mytilus californianus

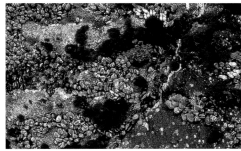

They're masters of their zone

Where waves pound the rocks, mussels outcompete all other animals and plants for space. But mussels can't take over completely, because ochre stars eat them. As these voracious sea stars munch mussels, they clear living space for algae, barnacles and others.

Don't eat 'em

From spring to fall, California mussels are quarantined because they may be poisonous, so you shouldn't eat them. As mussels take in great numbers of toxic dinoflagellates, they concentrate the poison. If you eat poisonous mussels, you could get sick and die.

Check with your county Health Department before you collect mussels.

Killers lurk in the mussel bed

Many animals fight for space along the rocky shore, but once mussels arrive the battle is lost. When a young mussel reaches the shore, it picks a spot among algae, barnacles or mussels, then anchors. As mussels grow, they slowly overshadow the algae and smother the barnacles. Eventually they develop massive communities and take over large areas of the middle intertidal zone.

It's eat or be eaten in the intertidal

Every diner could be dinner

Many animals lie low when a predator's around, hoping they won't be discovered. But when the predator gets too close, an animal may run away, rely on its armor or strike back. A predator, like a sea star, causes limpets to run down slopes and turban snails to tumble off ledges. To loosen a predator's grip, abalones rock and twist, then gallop away.

Pinto abalone
Haliotis kamtschatkana

Giant sea star
Pisaster giganteus

Sea hare
Aplysia californica

Sea lemon
Anisodoris nobilis

It makes off in a cloud

When startled, a sea hare sends out a confusing cloud of purple ink. They also escape predators by running away. Surprisingly quick, they can gallop four feet per minute.

Predators avoid bad taste

Sea slugs have very few predators. Their skin may secrete acid or poison or they may protect themselves with the stinging cells of anemones that they eat. The keyhole limpet expands a fleshy cloak, or mantle, over the shell at the approach of a sea star. This soft tissue may taste bad or prevent the sea star from getting a good grip.

Seaweeds fend off fishes with bad taste

Seaweeds don't have feet, teeth or claws, but some can defend themselves against grazers: they taste terrible. These seaweeds have chemicals, like acids and tannins, that discourage most nibblers.

While most hide, others find it pays to advertise

Pretty colors warn their predators sea slugs taste pretty bad

Brilliantly colored animals aren't trying to hide. They're telling predators "Beware: I'm not good to eat."

Nudibranches look delicate and vulnerable, but they're not defenseless. They release bad-tasting chemicals, or sting anything that takes a bite. One encounter with a nudibranch and the predator sees those bright colors as a warning sign.

Horned phidiana
Phidiana crassicornis

Animals struggle for a home by the sea

Before and after: how shade fades an anemone

Bright sunlight spurs the greening of an anemone by encouraging the algae in its tissues to grow. But in the shade, the algae languish, making the anemone go pale or blanch white.

For a home, an urchin digs itself into a hole

Using their spines and teeth, purple sea urchins slowly burrow into solid rock. Because they dig and grow over a lifetime, some urchins end up trapped in caves with too-small entrances.

Red sea urchin
Strongylocentrotus franciscanus

Do sea urchins have shells?

A sea urchin's "shell" isn't a shell, but a skeleton. It lies beneath the skin and is called a test. The urchin's ball-and-socket spines are based on those bumps, and its tube feet extend through the many pores.

Purple sea urchin
Strongylocentrotus purpuratus

Shields and weapons protect and repel

A crab uses strong claws, or pincers, to gather food and protect itself. If attacked, a porcelain crab attacks back with the pincers. During battle it can detach a pincer which keeps pinching while the crab scuttles away.

Sea urchins have clawlike pincers between their spines. These bite a sea star's tube feet when it touches. Some animals have body guards: a crab may carry a cover of stinging anemones.

Decorator crab
Loxorhynchus crispatus

Purple shore crab
Hemigrapsus nudus

Shore crab is a delicacy for birds, otters and others—no wonder a crab scampers into cracks so fast! Once inside, its purple spots blend with surrounding gravel and rocks.

diet: diatoms, algae
size: to 2 in. (56 mm)

Lined shore crab
Pachygrapsus crassipes

This crab's main defense is simple: at any sign of danger, it scuttles quickly into the nearest crevice. When cornered, it uses its claws, giving pause to even its largest enemies.

diet: algae, diatoms, organic particles
size: to 2 in. (5 cm)

Rock crab
Cancer antennarius

A rock crab cages hermit crabs with its body and legs, then uses crushing claws to crack away each hermit crab's shell.

diet: hermit crabs, invertebrates
size: to 4.5 in. (12 cm)

If food floated in the air, you could filter-feed, too

If you were a mussel or other filter-feeder, each breath you took would bring food. This trick works under water because the sea is like a gigantic bowl of soup. Many ocean animals like mussels, barnacles, tunicates and sea cucumbers have filters to collect food from the water.

Filter-feeding isn't easy—an oyster may have to filter eight gallons of water an hour to get a good meal.

A barnacle spends life on its head

When a barnacle larva lands on shore, it may "walk" around on its antennae looking for a suitable home. It glues its head to the perfect spot, lies on its back and uses its hairy legs to kick food into its mouth.

Giant acorn barnacle
Balanus nubilus

Under the volcano-shaped shell, a barnacle lies on its back and waits. When water rushes by, the barnacle stretches its feathery legs and kicks food down to its mouth.

diet: organic
particles, plankton
size: to 4.3 in. (11 cm)

Light-bulb tunicate
Clavelina huntsmani

Tunicates feed by pumping water through their gills. As water passes through a mucus-covered sieve, small bits of food are trapped, rolled into a string and passed to the mouth.

diet: phytoplankton, organic particles
size: to 2 in. (5 cm)

Orange sea cucumber
Cucumaria miniata

Nestled between the rocks is the orange sea cucumber. Mucus on its showy tentacles traps food. In "finger-licking" fashion the cucumber sticks each tentacle in its mouth to get its meal.

diet: plankton, organic particles
size: to 10 in. (25 cm)

Seaweeds are the plants of the sea

These plants thrive in sunlit, shallow waters

Like all plants, the large algae we call "seaweeds" need sunlight to grow. Since the sea gets too dim at about 150 feet, seaweeds grow only along the shore. Like intertidal animals, they live in bands, or zones. From the slippery blankets on rocks at low tide to the tangled clumps on the beach after a storm, seaweeds provide food and shelter for many.

Seaweeds struggle against the sun, surf and animals

Under the sun, *Porphyra* gets crisp and looks dead. But when the tide's in, it absorbs water and becomes supple again. The sea palm, *Postelsia,* is flexible enough to bounce back after being battered by waves. And while *Iridaea* lives where there's less drying and pounding, it must contend with many more grazers.

Sea palm
Postelsia palmaeformis

When there's no bare rock, sea palms will grow on other plants and animals. Storms often knock these assemblages off the rocks, providing new settling space for young sea palms.

Sea lettuce
Ulva sp.

Although thin and fragile looking, sea lettuce takes a lot of abuse— pounding waves and drying sun. These plants are "weeds": they quickly over-grow barren areas.

Mastocarpus
Mastocarpus papillatus

This plant grows in two different shapes, often living side-by-side. In one phase it's full and leafy; in the next, it's thin and crusty.

Corallina
Corallina vancouveriensis

This delicate-looking plant is able to withstand crashing waves. That's because it's made of strings of stony segments and soft, flexible ones.

Pelvetia
Pelvetia compressa

Under the rays of the sun, this seaweed dries and shrinks. The shrinking squeezes sacs in the branch tips, freeing eggs and sperm to slip into the sea when the tide returns.

Dead man's fingers
Codium fragile

The dark, spongy "fingers" of this seaweed dangle from the tops and sides of rocks. At one time they were used as packing material for shipping live marine invertebrates.

Iridescent weed
Mazzaella flaccida

Where broad blades drape the rocks and iridescent colors wave in the surge, beware. If you step on this slippery seaweed, you'll take a tumble.

How is a cow like a limpet?

Rough Limpet
Lottia scabra

These high intertidal limpets move about to graze during high tide on the thin film of algae and diatoms covering the rock. They return to their home scar after each grazing foray.

Both cows and limpets graze, but an owl limpet doesn't eat grass. It scrapes red algae off rocks with its tooth-covered tongue. Opal and iron deposits on the teeth give this tongue, or radula, the scraping power of mild steel. Rocks along the shore bear the marks of the radula.

Owl limpets graze algae on their farms

This limpet stakes out and tends a farm about 13 inches square. Protecting this farm from intruders, the owl limpet rasps barnacles off with its radula, bulldozing limpets, mussels and anemones with its shell. To avoid getting knocked loose by owl limpets, smaller limpets often climb up on their backs.

Opportunity rocks: a typical succession story

A typical intertidal succession story starts when a patch of rock in the surf zone is laid bare. Waves of species re-colonize it, all competing for the same small space. First come various algae. Barnacles replace the seaweeds and are themselves muscled out by the mussels. Sea palms grow atop the mussels, and all hang on till they're knocked off by a wave, and the rock is bared.

Space is in short supply

On rocky shores, animals need shelter from crashing waves, drying sun and hungry predators. Each seeks a place where it can eat, grow and reproduce. But setting up a home isn't simple—competition is fierce on these crowded shores. Barnacles and mussels wrestle for a rock to cling to. Limpets live on mussel shells; pea crabs live inside.

Blue top snail
Calliostoma ligatum

Goose barnacle
Pollicipes polymerus

There's safety in numbers

Periwinkles cluster together in cracks and crevices in the rocks. There they stay moist, while hiding from hungry shorebirds.

Checkered periwinkle
Littorina scutulata

Eroded periwinkle
Littorina keenae

Rough limpet
Macclintockia scabra

Seaweed limpet
Discurria insessa

Hermit crabs play the shell game

A hermit crab has a mobile home, too—it wears an empty snail shell to protect its soft body. But as the crab grows, it needs bigger and bigger shells. So hermit crabs often steal shells from each other and will even battle over a prized shell.

Hermit crab
Pagurus samuelis

The hermit crab looks for an empty snail shell, then packs that fortress on its back. Instead of scuttling into cracks when danger threatens, the crab pulls into its shell and bars the door with a claw.

diet: algae, organic particles
size: to 1 in. (19 mm)

Mobile homes offer shelter

Most animals make homes in whatever's available—under rocks, in crevices or among plants. A top snail doesn't have to look for a home; on its back is a shelter, complete with locking door. The door, or operculum, is fastened to the snail's foot. When the snail pulls its foot back in the shell, the operculum seals the opening.

Homing limpets fit right in

After feeding trips, a limpet returns to the same spot on its rock. Each limpet shapes its shell-edge to match its spot: a custom fit that lets it clamp down tight to conserve moisture.

Brown turban snail
Tegula brunnea

A turban snail's shell is not its castle. Barnacles and other creatures share the space, living on the turban snail's shell.

85

Some anemones engage in clone wars

Each cluster of aggregating anemones is made of clones—identical individuals split from a single parent. There are clear paths around each cluster because an anemone won't tolerate anyone but its clonemates. Contact between different clusters starts a fight: zapping one another with stinging cells, they battle till one retreats.

Clone enemies go down to stinging defeat

Anemone warriors store potent stinging cells in knobs that grow beneath their tentacles. When they lean over and stick it to an alien anemone, the cells explode into the enemy like a barrage of poison-tipped arrows.

Aggregating anemone
Anthopleura elegantissima, at high tide

Aggregating anemone
Anthopleura elegantissima, at low tide

Giant green anemone
Anthopleura xanthogrammica

This green plantlike creature is actually an animal with plants living inside it. Algae in the tissues of the anemone's gut provide extra nourishment and a bright green color.

diet: mussels, crabs, small fishes
size: to 7 in. (17 cm)

Rocks conceal some slippery types

Rocks make a hide-out for elusive characters known as blennies. These long, thin fishes can slip like snakes into cracks between the boulders. By keeping to these tight spaces, blennies avoid predators and keep cool till the tide comes in.

Monkeyface-eel
Cebidichthys violaceus

That fearsome face glaring from the rocks is just a front. Though the young are hunters, they grow up nonaggressive, becoming vegetarians that munch mostly algae.

diet: algae, invertebrates
size: to 30 in. (76 cm)

Rockweed gunnel
Xererpes fucorum

Gunnels of different colors all match their habitats. It's partly choice: a greenish fish seeks out green algae. And it's partly diet: eating red prey keeps a red gunnel red.

diet: molluscs, crustaceans
size: to 9 in. (23 cm)

Black prickleback
Xiphister atropurpureus

These fish stay in tide pools when the tide goes out. Their long, thin shape lets them fit under the rocks and between seaweeds, where there's water to keep them cool and moist.

diet: small invertebrates, fishes
size: to 1 ft. (30.5 cm)

One way to avoid danger is to avoid the enemy's eye

Many intertidal animals deceive their predators by matching the colors, shapes or shadows in their rocky homes. The zigzags on a lined chiton's back seem to break up its outline, making it disappear into the algae it crawls on. Green, red and brown kelpfishes use another tactic—they hover near green, red and brown algae. It's such a perfect match the fish is invisible till it moves.

Lined chiton
Tonicella lineata

Many animals sleep in mussel beds

Mussel beds provide shelter for about three hundred different security-seeking plants and animals. Worms and crabs hide among the tangled cables, or byssal threads. Whelks devour attached barnacles and limpets graze the algae-covered shells.

Mussel worm
Nereis grubei

Sea spider
Pycnogonum sp.

Isopod
Cirolana harfordi

Camouflaged animals play hide-and-seek in the rocks

Sculpins finish their rock act with special effects

Some fishes have leafy fins, skins or bristles that sway with the seaweeds growing on rocks. Tidepool sculpins act like rocks by lying very still. The fish moves in a sudden burst, then sits … all too quick to be seen.

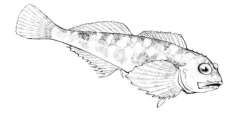

Umbrella crab
Cryptolithodes sitchensis

When this creature sits still, it hardly looks like a crab at all. That broad shell hides the telltale legs and claws and those splotches blend right into the scenery.

diet: calcareous algae
size: to 3.5 in. (9 cm)

Decorator crab
Loxorhynchus crispatus

To keep from becoming fish dinner, decorator crabs use camouflage. The young cover their shells with seaweed and other debris, costuming themselves to resemble long-legged rocks.

diet: algae, sponges, small crustaceans
size: to 4 in. (10 cm)

Woolly sculpin
Clinocottus analis

Perched like birds in "branches" of algae, woolly sculpins become one with the shrubbery. Fringes and bristles fuzz their outline, letting them blend in.

diet: invertebrates
size: to 7 in. (18 cm)

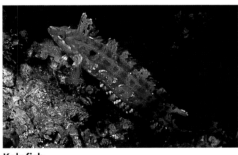

Kelpfish
Gibbonsia sp.

With a wave of its fins, this fish vanishes into the algae. If the fish turns sideways, you'll see another illusion: "eyes" stare from its side, while its real eyes are hidden from sight.

diet: small invertebrates, algae
size: to 4 in. (10 cm)

Animals practice all kinds of love on the rocks

Hooked slipper snail
Crepidula adunca

Mobile males and females mate

Not all intertidal animals have fixed sexes: a slipper snail changes from male to female as it grows, and a sea slug is both male and female. But most mating involves a male fertilizing the eggs of a female. Some animals put their energy into producing many eggs, then ignore them; some produce few eggs, but tend to them carefully. In the intertidal, both strategies work.

Slipper snails live in stacks

Hooked slipper snails will stack on the back of a bigger snail. A male slipper snail is drawn to a female by her scent and rides atop her until he turns into a female. All hooked slipper snails go through this sex change as they age.

Giant green anemone
Anthopleura xanthogrammica

Like many marine animals, these anemones reproduce by casting their seed to the sea. The larvae drift far and wide with the currents before settling down.

diet: mussels, crabs, small fishes
size: to 7 in. (17 cm)

Some animals multiply by dividing

Though it helps to be fixed to a rock when waves pound you, you're stuck when you need a mate. Some animals solve this problem by reproducing without partners; they simply make clones. Aggregating anemones split—where there was one, now there are two. Sponges can bud off pieces of themselves to make little sponges.

Mother anemone broods till the young leave home

When these tiny anemones were just larvae, they crawled out of their mother's mouth and settled on her column. They'll stay there protected till they're juveniles, ready to go off on their own.

Strawberry anemone
Corynactis californica

Proliferating anemone
Epiactis prolifera

Long-distance sex is the norm

Abalones, sea urchins and sea anemones don't waste energy looking for mates. They just cast incredible numbers of eggs and sperm into the sea. Eggs meet sperm by chance, and the fertilized eggs become larvae. But life as a larva is tough; most get eaten, can't find food or a suitable home. In this numbers game, a species wins only if enough of its young survive to replace adults that die.

Red abalone
Haliotis rufescens

Sea hare
Aplysia californica

Plainfin midshipman
Porichthys notatus

Each sea hare is both male and female, but they still need to mate. Dozens pile up for sea hare orgies. They mate in lines and circles: each is male to the one in front and female to the one behind.

diet: algae, eelgrass
size: to 16 in. (40 cm)

These fish scoop out a nest under a rock, then attach up to 500 eggs to the ceiling. The male midshipman guards the nest till the young have hatched and grown large enough to leave home.

diet: fishes, crustaceans
size: to 15 in. (38 cm)

The Coastal Stream

Streams create
thin corridors of water
in a dry land

Stream life's all wet

Lush tangles of trees, vines and shrubs crowd their banks, splurging on year-round moisture. The plants shade the streams and provide habitat for turtles, newts and other residents. When steelhead salmon are ready to spawn, they leave the ocean to swim up these freshwater coastal streams.

COASTAL STREAM

Horsetail
Equisetum sp.

◄ *Salmon are born in freshwater rivers, then swim to the salty sea where they spend most of their lives. As adults, they return to the river to lay eggs, finding their way to home streams from thousands of miles out in the ocean.*

Salmon make a heroic odyssey to the sea and back

Each fall, salmon return from scattered ocean haunts to the coastal streams of their birth. Salmon fight their way upstream to lay and fertilize their eggs. After hatching, the young return to the sea, continuing the ancient cycle. Salmon may make this journey for several seasons, but die, exhausted, after their first spawning.

Eggs

The female fish digs a series of shallow nests. After the eggs she lays are fertilized by her mate, she covers them with gravel. Seven or eight weeks later, the eggs hatch.

Alevin

After hatching, the young fishes remain under the gravel for several weeks, living off their leftover yolk. When the yolk is gone, they wriggle up through the gravel as fry.

Fry

Salmon fry spend one to three years in their streams, eating small prey and being eaten by birds, snakes and larger fishes. Only one in ten survives to enter the ocean.

Smolt

As the fishes migrate to the ocean, they go through a change of life that fits them to live in salt water. They also change colors, the better to blend into the ocean.

Ocean-run adults

Once at sea, the fishes may travel thousands of miles. After two to three years they head home to spawn, guided by magnetic cues and the unique scent of their home streams.

Spawning adults

As salmon make their way back up the streams, they undergo another transformation. Their color changes, and the males grow hooked jaws, some with fanglike teeth. After spawning, they die.

When is a trout not a trout?

When it's gone to sea, a rainbow trout is known as a steelhead salmon. Some trout never leave home, but migrate between stream and lake. These may change colors, but aren't called steelhead salmon.

Coastal Stream

Rainbow trout lead a double life

Clear-flowing, freshwater streams hide rainbow trout in their pools and riffles. But streams are only one part of the trout's life: when the fish are two years old, they go to sea. They venture halfway across the north Pacific, feasting on the ocean's bounty.

These fish go against the flow

Rainbow trout that have been to sea earn a new name: steelhead salmon. After two years, they return to their home streams and struggle upriver to spawn. Swimming upstream is second nature to trout. They face into the current and even try leaping up the waterfall.

The Coastal Stream

A good stream is hard to find

Many streams along our coast have been damaged by human activities. Dams alter streams so they can't support fishes, and poorly-managed construction and logging can clog fishes' nesting sites with silt. As a result, wild steelhead salmon populations have plummeted.

Today, people are working to restore stream habitat and to hatch and release native steelhead salmon.

There's lots of green along a stream

Plants growing beside coastal streams usually have large, broad leaves that can gather lots of sunlight. With plenty of water available, plants grow quickly.

Fishes mate and lay eggs here

Steelhead salmon lay their eggs in the gravelly bottoms of cool, fast-running streams. If the streams become clogged with silt, these fishes can't reproduce successfully.

Storm-gorged streams flatten plants

With winter rains, a peaceful stream can become a churning brown current. The flood can flatten and uproot streamside plants, but most of the plants spring back up or re-root after the storm.

Red-legged frog
Rana aurora

This frog is seldom seen: it stays hidden under logs, leaves and the like. But hiding doesn't always save it from non-native bullfrogs—hungry predators that eat up native frogs.

diet: insects, worms
size: to 5 in. (13 cm)

Sacramento sucker
Catostomus occidentalis

The sucker searches river bottoms for food, feeling about with sensitive lips. Its mouth reaches down like a vacuum hose, sucking up mud with algae, worms and other food.

diet: algae, invertebrates
size: to 19.5 in. (50 cm)

Hitch
Lavinia exilicauda

People usually think minnows are finger-sized fishes, but there's a hitch: this one can grow to be more than a foot. And hitch are only medium-size minnows—some family members are five feet or more.

diet: plankton, insects
size: to 14 in. (36 cm)

Rainbow trout
Oncorhynchus mykiss

Lurking in pools under falling water, the larger, aggressive trout snap up insects swept over the waterfall. Smaller trout, crowded out to the water's edge, catch what they can among the logs and ledges.

diet: insects, larvae, small fishes
size: to 3.5 ft. (1.1 m)

Crayfish
Pacifastacus sp.

Crayfish are like small, freshwater lobsters. Careful—those big claws are bruisers! The crayfish uses them both for defense and crushing food. Smaller claws on its front legs also tear up food.

diet: plants, organic matter, snails
size: to 4.5 in. (11 cm)

Silver salmon
Oncorhynchus kisutch

Juvenile salmon migrate to the ocean to mature, then return to the same stream to spawn.

diet: crayfish, insects, small fishes
size: to 3 ft. (98 cm)

Sacramento squawfish
Ptychocheilus grandis

Till it's grown, the squawfish swims in the midwater and eats insects. But a young squawfish is already the shape of things to come. The long body and big mouth mark a hunter who'll lie in wait, then lunge at prey.

diet: insects, crayfish, fishes
size: to 4 ft. (1.2 m)

Western pond turtle
Clemmys marmorata

In the morning, look for these turtles lounging on the log. Their sun-bathing has an aim: turtles need to soak up sun to raise their body temperatures. When it's warmer, they take to the water.

diet: plants, animals, organic matter
size: to 7.5 in. (19 cm)

Threespine stickleback
Gasterosteus aculeatus

A thumb-sized stickleback won't get much bigger. Though it'd fit in the mouth of many a predator, this fish isn't favored prey. Stiff spines on its back and belly make it a prickly meal.

diet: invertebrates, fishes
size: to 3 in. (8 cm)

Horsetail
Equisetum sp.

This plant usually grows near water along coastal streams. The long, jointed stems are hollow and rough to the touch because they contain tiny, sandlike crystals.

Size: to 4 ft. (1.2 m)

COASTAL STREAM

Sea Otters
along the rocky coast

*Wrapped in ribbons of kelp,
a sea otter floats on the surface of
Monterey Bay. Buoyed on the
ocean's swells, it sleeps cradled in the
canopy of the kelp forest.*

In swaying undersea forests, otters and kelp flourish together

Deep within the forest below lie the otter's sun-dappled hunting grounds—rich with crabs, urchins and abalone. But otters do more than hunt among the kelp fronds. By eating urchins and other kelp-grazers, they can help keep the kelp forest growing lush and thick.

Along our rocky coast, the otters' lives are woven into the fabric of the kelp forest community.

◄ *This female otter is grooming herself off the shores of Monterey Harbor.*

99

Fur hunters nearly doomed sea otters here

Once, sea otters lived all along the Pacific coast. But in the late 1700s, Russian, American and European fur traders began to hunt here. Seeking wealth from furs, these commercial hunters drove otters to the brink of extinction in just 100 years.

Only a few California sea otters survived the hunting

By the early 1900s, most people thought otters were extinct in California. But along the remote Big Sur coast, a group of about 50 otters had escaped the hunters. The otters living in the bay today (and in our exhibit) are the descendants of those fortunate few.

From a small group of survivors near Big Sur, the population of California sea otters has grown to more than 2,100 today.

The aquarium is working to understand and protect sea otters

Otters have made a comeback along our coast, but their future's still uncertain. The aquarium is studying the biology of our exhibit sea otters and sea otters in the bay. What we learn will help us protect sea otters in the future.

Our Otter Family Album

Once hungry, Hailey's now healthy

Found stranded on Carmel Beach, Hailey was weak from hunger after becoming separated from her mother. The three-week-old pup was brought to the aquarium, where a round-the-clock crew of staff and volunteers nursed her back to health.

Roscoe wasn't ready for a wild life

Husbandry staff raised Roscoe to be the first otter we returned to the sea. But six days after his release, a tired, skinny Roscoe was brought back to the aquarium. He never learned to forage on his own. We've since taught other orphaned otters the skills for survival in the wild.

Goldie thrived on clams and care

Separated from her mother when she was five weeks old, a frail, sick Goldie drifted ashore at Asilomar Beach in early 1984. But, set up on a waterbed at the aquarium, fed clam-and-cream milkshakes 12 times daily and lovingly groomed, she recovered quickly.

Sea otters are at home in the kelp

Otters feast on the forest's bounty

From the water's surface to the seafloor below, kelp forests teem with life. California's sea otters feast on the bounty they find there and on the sandy seafloor. From abalone to urchins, otters in the bay eat more than 50 kinds of invertebrates (though each otter picks just a few favorite kinds of food).

Sea otter
Enhydra lutris

Otters help keep our forests lush

By eating kelp-munching sea urchins, otters help keep the balance of the bay's kelp forests from being overgrazed. When local otters were hunted nearly to extinction, the forests were more sparse in some areas. But when otters returned to the bay, the forests flourished—providing more habitat for a whole community of creatures.

Kelp helps anchor resting otters

Kelp provides a haven for otters. The sea's calmer among the groves. And otters often sleep wrapped in kelp fronds, which keep the otters from drifting away.

Sea otters gather in rafts

Sea otters often rest in groups called rafts. Rafts of two to 12 otters—mothers, pups and territorial males—are common in the kelp beds just off the shoreline.

Otters hunt in coastal waters

Hunting in the kelp forests along our coast, sea otters feast on more than 50 kinds of crabs, snails, urchins and other invertebrates. But from this wide choice of prey, each otter usually picks just a few favorite foods.

Look for otters out in the bay

Sea otters spend about half the day resting. You'll also find them sleeping on rocks or floating quietly on their backs.

A sea otter dines at the surface

An otter may hunt on the seafloor, but always returns to the surface to eat. Floating there on its back, it uses its chest as a table. (And if dinner's crab or clam, the otter may use a rock to crack open its prey.)

Otters feel for their meals

Sea otters feel movements under water through their long whiskers—which helps them sense moving prey even in murky water. And they use their sensitive forepaws to probe the rocky seafloor to find prey hidden there.

Sea otters hunt high and low

Amid forests of kelp, sea otters hunt from the fronds floating on the surface to the holdfasts anchored below. Sea otters can dive 300 feet deep, but most otters along our coast hunt in waters less than 100 feet deep.

An otter's coat has pockets

A sea otter's coat comes with handy pockets: flaps of skin under each front leg. An otter uses them to stash prey during a dive, which leaves its paws free to hunt some more.

Bubbles flow from otters' fur

The tiny air bubbles an otter grooms into its fur help keep its coat waterproof. But when the otter dives, some air escapes and streams to the surface. Later, when the otter grooms again, it'll work air bubbles back into its fur.

Tumbling otters may be playing

Play is an important part of a young sea otter's day. Otters often dive together, wrestling and chasing one another in the water. They can also be seen quietly grooming each other.

An otter's survival depends on successful hunting

Pink abalone
Haliotis corrugata

Seafood warms an otter's heart

To stay warm in cold water, a sea otter burns calories at nearly three times the rate you do. An otter fuels its fast metabolism by eating up to a third of its weight in food a day. (A 150-pound person would have to eat 50 pounds of food a day to match that!)

An otter's tool kit

When a sea otter needs to pry loose an abalone or crack open a crab, a stone or an old shell may do the trick. Otters learn to use these simple tools to gather and subdue prey.

Hunting skills take time to learn

A sea otter pup learns to hunt from its mother. Mastering the skills to capture a spiny sea urchin or a wriggling octopus can be a trial. And pups make errors along the way—"catching" rocks instead of rock crabs or empty shells instead of snails. But after six months, most pups can hunt on their own.

Sea otters' fur has meant life and death

An otter's coat cuts the ocean's chill

An otter needs protection against chilly ocean waters. While some marine mammals have a thick layer of fat to keep out the cold, a sea otter is wrapped in the world's densest fur— a luxurious double-layer coat. That coat needs care—an otter spends hours cleaning and grooming to keep its fur waterproof.

Fine fur brought sea otters close to extinction

The luxurious fur that keeps otters warm in cold waters can keep people warm in cold winters. In the 1700s, high prices for otter fur in Europe and America spurred a relentless hunt for otters. Before the hunting began, some 200,000 otters lived along the coast from Mexico to Alaska. When the hunting ended in 1911, fewer than 2,000 otters remained.

Sea otter fur is the thickest in the world

At its thickest, sea otter fur is made up of more than a million hairs per square inch (the average is 250,000 hairs per square inch). The dense fur has two layers: inch-long underfur and inch-and-a-half-long guard hairs.

California's otters face an uncertain future

Their comeback has been slow

Sea otters once lived from Mexico to Alaska. Now, California sea otters live along a stretch of coast less than 200 miles long. Their population's grown—from some 50 otters in 1900 to more than 2,100 today. But with more people living along the coast, otters face threats from pollution and drowning in nets.

Oil and otters don't mix

Oil spills are the biggest threat to California sea otters. Oil destroys the insulating properties of otters' fur and poisons them as they groom. A major spill off the central California coast could foul the entire range of California sea otters and doom them to extinction here.

Our lives are intertwined

The relationships between people, sea otters and kelp forests are all very complex. By studying these relationships, we've already learned a lot. But many questions must still be answered before we can fully protect otters and our other precious coastal resources.

Otters rest half the day

Sea otters spend about half of each day resting. In the bay they nap floating on their backs, wrapped in kelp to keep from drifting away.

Otters swim on their backs

Sea otters usually swim on their backs at the surface. Paddling with their flipperlike rear paws, they cruise at two to three miles per hour—about as fast as some people swim.

Some otters steal their meals

Instead of foraging for prey, some sea otters steal their meals from others. Pups snatch morsels from their mothers. And adult males grab food from just about any otter they can bully.

Otters at the aquarium eat a varied diet

Our otters eat a varied diet of squid, fish, shrimp and clams. They also get occasional treats like abalone, whole crabs and blades of kelp.

Otters rest paws-up to stay warm

Sea otters often float on their backs, forepaws sticking out of the water and hindflippers curled up over their bellies. Why? Their paws aren't well insulated, and the ocean's colder than the air above, so resting paws-up helps sea otters stay warm.

A heads-up otter's on the lookout

A sea otter can see well, both above and below the surface. To scan its surroundings, an otter pokes its head straight up out of the water and stares. Its called "periscoping."

Good grooming keeps otters warm

A rubbing, rolling, scratching sea otter is busy cleaning its fur. This grooming coats its fur with natural oils from the skin and fluffs it up with fine air bubbles. It's worth the effort: fluffy fur is insulated and waterproof, so a well-groomed otter stays warm.

SEA OTTERS

Sea Otters

Red sea urchin
Strongylocentrotus franciscanus

SEA OTTERS

Turban snail
Tegula brunnea

How long do sea otters live?

Male sea otters usually live to be 10 to 15 years old. Females live longer, sometimes 20 years or more.

Roscoe's our largest otter

At the aquarium, Roscoe is the largest otter on exhibit. You can identify him by his broad face, dark color and wide nose.

How fast do otters swim?

Paddling along as they float on their backs, otters swim about two miles per hour. But when they dive, they swim on their bellies and travel twice as fast.

Goldie's named for golden fur

Goldie, the aquarium's female otter, can be identified by the patches of golden fur near her cheeks. She's shy around people, but bold enough to steal food from the other otters.

What do sea otters eat?

California sea otters eat slow-moving, bottom-dwelling invertebrates like abalones, sea urchins, snails and crabs.

Hailey's streaked with gray

You can recognize Hailey at the aquarium by her light-colored fur and the streaks of gray around her head. (In otters, gray fur doesn't necessarily mean old age.)

Tumbling otters may be playing

At the aquarium, our playful otters often wrestle and chase each other. But if you see the largest otter biting another's nose, that's Roscoe, our male, trying to mate.

Why do otters scratch?

Otters aren't scratching because they itch; they're grooming. This keeps their fur waterproof and clean.

We still have much to learn about otters

We're learning more about sea otters

At the aquarium, scientists watch and record the otters' behaviors. Our scientists also study otters' biology and health. The more we learn from our otters, the better we can protect their wild kin.

Despite protection, wild California sea otters are still in danger

Although laws protect them from hunting and a marine sanctuary protects their habitat, California sea otters are still at risk. Oil from a single tanker spill near San Francisco Bay—or off the central coast—could wipe out the entire population.

What we learn today may save otters in the future

If an oil spill wipes out sea otters in the wild, our otters and those at other aquariums and zoos could help re-establish a wild population. That's why it's important to study and understand the reproductive biology and genetics of our otters.

That's not a dinosaur

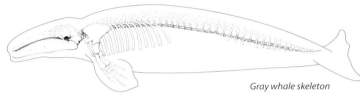

Gray whale skeleton

In the aquarium's Marine Mammal gallery you'll find bare bones that were once a whale.

The skeleton is what's left of a young gray whale that washed onto a Monterey beach in 1980.

From whale to display took over two years. We removed the bones and buried them for a year of cleaning by decay. After another year of washing and soaking the skeleton, we carefully reassembled it, bone by bone.

Whales need skeletons

A whale's skeleton doesn't support the whale's weight; the water does. The skeleton acts as an anchor for the muscles. The centers of a whale's bones are spongy and filled with fat, making them lighter than those of land mammals. A large skull protects the brain and supports the baleen plates, which trap prey.

Whales have finger bones

Most whales have the same bones in their front flippers that we have in our hands and arms. The bones are shorter and flatter, and the muscle and skin surrounding them make paddlelike flippers, used for steering and stability. A whale's ribs don't close around the chest the way our ribs do; this allows the chest to collapse during deep dives.

There's not much to a whale's skeleton

You don't see a whale's broad tail flukes because they have no bones, only muscle and connective tissue. Even though they evolved from land animals with four legs, whales don't have hind legs. If you look for two small bones hanging beneath the tail, you'll see all that remains of the hind legs and pelvis.

MARINE GALLERY

The Marine Mammal Gallery

▲ *Gray whales have been seen in the summer months off Vancouver Island. They seem to return to the same feeding areas each year.*

Gray whale
Eschrichtius robustus

▲ *Biologists can tell individual grays apart from their patterns of barnacle clusters—no two are alike.*

Gray whale

Gray whale
Eschrichtius robustus

These whales swim a long round-trip

Each year, gray whales travel from the Arctic to Mexican lagoons and back—at 12,000 miles, the longest migration made by any mammal. They spend summer feeding in cold Arctic waters. In the fall, the whales head south to breed and give birth. Females give birth in the shallow lagoons and nurse their thousand-pound calves. Come spring, they turn north again.

Because they swim close to shore during this migration, gray whales can be seen off the California coast from November through April.

Migrating grays are easy to follow

These whales have a regular swimming and breathing pattern. They surface from a dive, take three to five breaths, then raise their tail flukes and dive for three to five minutes.

Gray whales start life in warm shallows

Most female gray whales mate one year and give birth the next, after a year of pregnancy.

Newborn calves are dark, wrinkled and barnacle-free. In the lagoon the calf remains in close contact with its mother, often swimming onto her tail flukes. Before making the trip north, the baby grows and fattens on 50 gallons of milk a day.

To eat, gray whales suck in silt

During the summer, gray whales feed in icy Arctic seas, eating mostly bottom-living crustaceans, worms and molluscs. Using a mouthful of strainers, or baleen, gray whales filter their food from bottom sand and mud.

The gray whale vacuums its meals from the seafloor. Lying on its side, the whale sucks loose sand and mud into its mouth. Then it strains the mouthful of muck through its fringed baleen filter, to separate dirt from dinner.

Feeding gray whales muddy the water

After feeding on the bottom, a gray whale surfaces with clouds of mud streaming from its mouth.

Dolphins

Common dolphin
Delphinus delphis

Here's a dolphin of a different color

Striking geometric patterns and yellowish side patches make this the most colorful dolphin. This coloring earned it other names, like "hourglass," "crisscross" and "saddleback" dolphin.

Surfing dolphins ride the waves

These dolphins are familiar companions to sailors of many seas. As fast-moving ships slice through the water, common dolphins surf alongside. Dolphins also use this hitchhiking trick with their own cousins: sometimes they ride on the waves of large whales.

Pacific white-sided dolphin
Lagenorhynchus obliquidens

These dolphins keep close company

White-sided dolphins swim in herds numbering in the thousands. Members form a close-knit group and will often care for a sick or injured dolphin.

Animals that live in such big social groups develop ways to keep in touch. Each dolphin identifies itself by a unique name-whistle. Staying close helps, too. Young dolphins communicate with a touch of a flipper as they swim beside adults.

MARINE GALLERY

111

Harbor porpoise

Harbor porpoise
Phocoena phocoena

These reclusive locals are rarely seen

Harbor porpoises live year-round in Monterey Bay. They usually travel alone or in small groups. Though they swim near shore, they're shy and seen less often than many offshore dolphins.

Because they live so close to shore, these animals face dangers from both pollution and net fishing. Harbor porpoises are also hunted in many parts of the world, and so their numbers have dwindled.

How do a porpoise and dolphin differ?

Ancient Romans called these little round whales porcus piscus, or pigfish. From this comes our word "porpoise." Porpoises tend to be smaller, stockier and shorter-faced than dolphins.

Hubbs' beaked whale
Mesoplodon carlhubbsi

Mystery whales keep scientists guessing

This is one of the most mysterious of all whales; scientists know little about it. No one's ever seen one riding a boat's bow wave or leaping in the air, as many dolphins do.

Much of what we do know comes from studying dead whales washed up on beaches. Most of them have long scars and scratches on their backs, which may be from fights between males.

Beaked whales make do with two teeth

Like most beaked whales, this whale has only two teeth. As they're perched outside the mouth, the tusks can't be very useful for feeding, but they're probably used for battle by the males.

Orca

Orca
Orcinus orca

That smile gave the orca its name

Orcas, or killer whales, have forty to fifty strong cone-shaped teeth that curve toward the throat and interlock like a zipper.

Whales leap from the sea

Sometimes whales jump out of the water and crash back into the sea. No one knows why they jump. This breach may be part of their courtship, a signal to distant whales, a way to remove parasites, or they may breach for fun.

An orca clan takes care of its own

Orcas live in tightknit family groups, or pods, of two to thirty individuals. With squeals and moans, pod members keep in touch. They will protect one another from danger and come to the aid of an ailing or injured companion. The pod moves from place to place as food sources change with the seasons.

Orcas are the wolves of the sea

Because the pod hunts like a wolf pack, orcas can go after any marine animal they want. They can encircle a school of fish, grab a seal from a sand bar, or harass a mighty blue whale to death. These hunting techniques, combined with swift speed and interlocking teeth, make the orca a top predator.

Orcas are dressed to kill

The distinctive black-and-white coloration of the orca is a type of camouflage. In the water, the dark and light patterns break up the shape of the body, and so a seal may not see an orca coming until it's too late.

MARINE GALLERY

Scuba diver

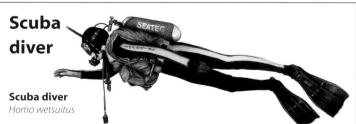

Scuba diver
Homo wetsuitus

Imitation whales swim our shores

This peculiar-looking creature is possibly a very primitive whale, not quite ready for life in the water: its nostrils are located in front of its face, instead of on top of its head.

This species needs to breathe many times each minute, and must carry an air supply under water. Still largely land animals, scuba divers must come ashore to mate and raise their young.

Divers do it slower

Even with double fins, scuba divers swim only half as fast as a gray whale at cruising speed. They're quite agile with their front feet, though, and use tools with an ability that rivals the clever sea otter.

Discover a wide-open world

Beyond the shelter of Monterey Bay stretches wide-open water. Here is a world without visible walls: there are no reefs or beaches; the bottom is far below. Waves and currents travel unchecked for miles, and there's nothing but water wherever you look.

Life's in constant motion

Flashing schools of tuna streak through these waters, swimming endlessly. Jellies pulse slowly, adrift on flowing currents. Animals here never come to rest. Whether they swim or drift, they spend their lives on the move, in this blue world of wide-open spaces.

Life keeps on moving

In the wide Pacific waters beyond Monterey Bay, life's in constant motion. Flashing schools of tuna streak by, swimming endlessly. Graceful jellies pulse slowly, adrift on flowing currents. Whether they swim or drift, animals here keep moving, never settling.

It's a wide-open world

Out there beyond the sheltering arms of the bay, it's a whole different

world. There's nothing but water wherever you look. There are no reefs, no beaches; the bottom lies far below. In these fluid, wide-open spaces, life ranges widely as conditions shift and change.

Anchovies set the water sparkling

Sun shines down into the clear blue water of the outer bay. It dances and flashes, lighting a quicksilver school of anchovies. The countless small fish form a living stream that shifts and flows through the sunlit sea.

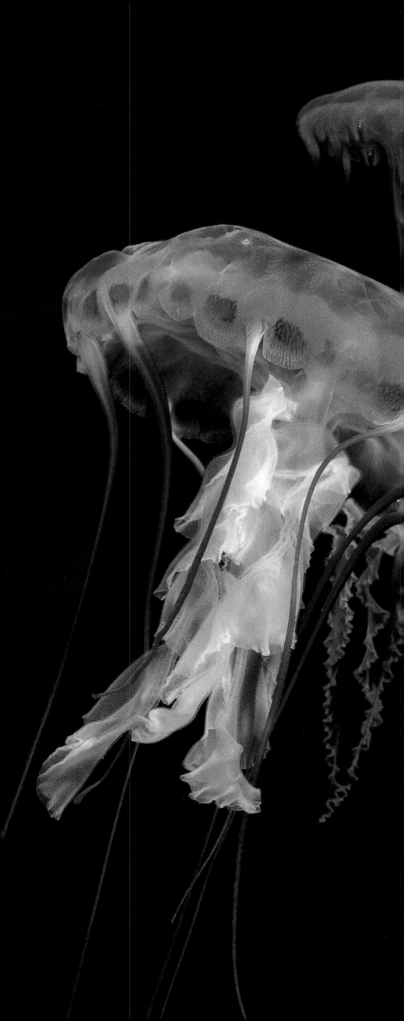

Outer Bay Life

Life in the Outer Bay

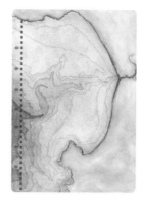

*Sixty miles out, Monterey Bay
gives way to the open waters*

Swift swimmers and graceful drifters share these waters

Sail west, past the bay's outer edge, till you see blue all around you. Here, where the bay meets the ocean past the continental shelf, you'll find the open waters, the largest habitat on Earth. At first, it all looks the same. But go below the surface and find currents warm and cold, areas nearly barren and areas rich with life.

Silver anchovies and sleek mackerel swim with ease; transparent jellies drift with the currents, traveling the seas. Swimmer and drifter alike live in a world of constant motion—a world with no visible walls and nowhere to hide.

Pacific mackerel
Scomber japonicus

◄ *Purple-striped jellies pulse along in the ocean's currents.*

How can they survive out in the open?

Northern anchovy
Engraulis mordax

Anchovies find safety in numbers

Anchovies, small fish that supply supper for many other fishes, swim in schools of thousands. Why stay in schools? Maybe the silvery flashing of so many fish confuses the anchovies' enemies. With all those moving targets, it's hard to focus on just one.

They don't play "follow the leader"

Schooling fish act like members in a marching band, moving as one. To coordinate these maneuvers, each

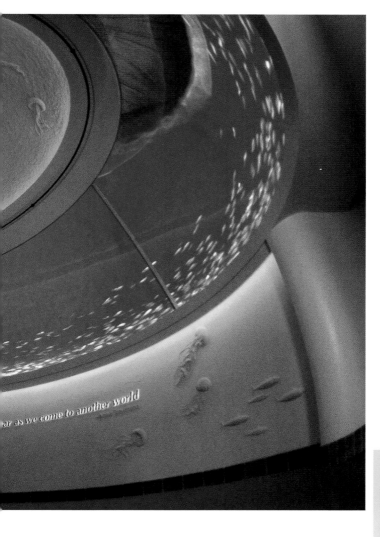

fish keeps an eye on its neighbor, using sight and pressure waves to determine its next move. As they turn, fish in the lead find themselves on the flanks.

Two-tone bodies help them vanish

These fish are dark on top and light beneath? This countershading helps hide them from predators. A predator looking up might not see silver bellies against the light sea surface; a predator looking down might miss dark backs against the dark below.

Anchovies at mealtime

As anchovies swim, they open wide, straining tiny plant and animal plankton from the water.

Northern anchovy
Engraulis mordax

Drifters

Purple-striped jelly
Pelagia colorata

Jellies drift through open waters

In certain seasons, when the currents run just right, purple-striped jellies mysteriously appear near the shores of Monterey. When the jellies arrive, it's wise to keep your distance (their sting isn't fatal, but it can be painful). Since divers have seen ocean sunfish eating these jellies, we know some fishes must be immune to the sting.

Drifters ride the ocean's highways

Up and down along our coast, past Monterey Bay, currents flow like rivers through the sea. Swift, strong fishes can swim against these currents, but plants and many animals just go with the flow. These drifters, called plankton, don't swim—they ride. But by catching the currents, they can travel far and wide.

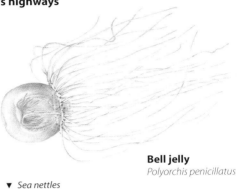

Bell jelly
Polyorchis penicillatus

▼ *Sea nettles*

Drifters

Strange-seeming drifters survive in a wide world

Some drifters are tiny; others are as big as beach balls; many have fantastic forms. All make the most of their open-water home. A jelly's soft body, with no bones or shell, is carried easily by the currents. Jellies often are transparent or tinged with blue, which helps them disappear from view.

The strange-seeming drifters are at home in a world very different from our own.

Jellies drift through open seas

Because it takes so little energy, drifting is the most economical way to travel the vast open waters. Drifting jellies need only pulse their bells gently as they ride the ocean's currents. As they go, they feed on small fishes, jellies and other small drifters also along for the ride.

They're built to go with the flow

Alien as it looks, a jelly's soft shape is perfectly adapted to its environment. The animal's thin skin stretches over a body that's more than 95% water (no bones or shells to weigh it down). And as the jelly drifts, those dangling tentacles, covered with stinging cells, are combing the water to catch its prey.

Sea nettle
Chrysaora fuscescens

Crystal jelly
Aequorea victoria

DRIFTERS

Jellies are simply beautiful

Watching a jelly up close, you can see it's not a fish—it has no bones, no fins. A jelly's a very simple animal.

The pulsing umbrella is its body. Underneath are lacy mouth-arms; hidden up inside them is the jelly's mouth. And from the rim trail graceful, stinging tentacles.

Lion's mane jelly
Cyanea capillata

Lobed comb jelly
Bolinopsis infundibulum

This comb jelly spreads out to dine

As this comb jelly drifts on the currents, it spreads two broad lobes out like nets to catch food. Tiny prey stick to the lobes, like flies to a spider's web. Then the food's swept by fine, little hairs toward the center, to the comb jelly's waiting mouth.

Sea gooseberry
Pleurobrachia bachei

This drifter casts a line for food

The sea gooseberry has a pair of long feathery tentacles it trails in the currents to trawl for food. It goes fishing for little drifters: animal plankton the size of specks. When plankton hit the tentacles, they're caught by special sticky cells; then the sea gooseberry reels in its meal.

Sea nettle
Chrysaora fuscescens

This jelly's tentacles are a sure sting

Not all jellies sting, but the sea nettle does. It hunts tiny drifting animals by trailing those long tentacles and frilly mouth-arms, all covered with stinging cells. When the tentacles touch prey, the stinging cells paralyze it and stick tight. From there the prey's moved to the mouth-arms and finally the mouth, where the prey's digested.

DRIFTERS

125

If you made a six-inch jelly as big as an umbrella, you'd see how it's built to drift

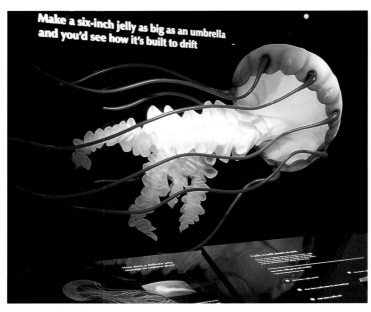

Make a six-inch jelly as big as an umbrella and you'd see how it's built to drift

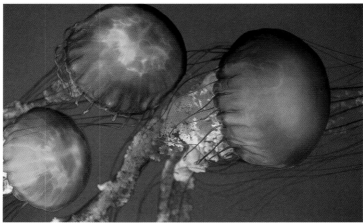

A jelly is built simply to drift

Without excess baggage like bones, brains or teeth, a jelly is free to drift with the currents. That light, simple body has all the equipment it needs to survive—to move about, sense its surroundings and capture and eat prey.

How to build the perfect drifter? Make it out of "jelly"

A jelly isn't flesh and bone like most animals you know; a jelly's body is made of a material that's like Jello. Although that may seem delicate, it's great material for a drifter. It won't sink or float, so the animal can stay steady when it catches a current. And it's transparent, so the animal can hide by blending in with its surroundings.

Purple-striped jelly
Pelagia colorata

How does a jelly move?

The bell pulses to move short distances—to go farther, a jelly rides currents.

How does a jelly sense its surroundings?

Sense organs detect light, tell the jelly which way is up and allow it to "taste" the water.

How does a jelly eat?

Tentacles stretch out to sting and trap drifting food, then contract to pull it in.
　　Mouth-arms carry food from the tentacles to the mouth.
　　The mouth opens into the gut.
　　The gut digests the food.

How does a jelly reproduce?

Sex organs produce eggs (in females) or sperm (in males).

What gives a jelly substance?

A Jello-like material makes up the bulk of a jelly's body.

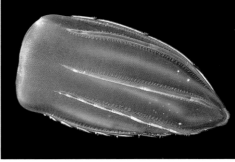

Comb jelly
Beröe forskali

DRIFTERS

Tiny Drifters

Look closely . . .

A drop of sea water's full of life. Focus in, and see a hidden world: tiny plants, larval crabs and fishes, all living in an endless tale of eat-and-be-eaten.

It's a world of tiny drifters

These are the sea's tiniest drifters—plankton so small they're hard to see. The outer bay teems with billions and billions; they make a vital, nearly invisible community.

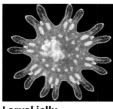

Larval jelly

Fish larva

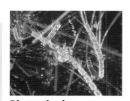

Phytoplankton

Copepods

Crab larva

There's a world in every drop

Peer into a magnified drop of sea water and you'll find it's swimming with magical life: young crabs in spiked disguise, armored animals, plants in glass pillboxes. These are plankton—tiny drifters of every sort and form that fill a little-known world.

Tiny drifters come in huge numbers

Take this drop of sea water, multiply it times all the gallons of sea water in the outer bay and you'll see there must be billions and billions of tiny drifters. They're so small you can barely see them, but their numbers are immense. Eaten by animals from anchovies to whales, they feed the entire sea.

What lives in a drop of sea water?

Copepods are food for many larger animals. **Diatoms** and dinoflagellates are tiny plants. **Larval crabs** drift for many weeks, then settle. **Fish eggs** of many species drift until they hatch.

Shifting clouds of drifters fill the sea

The currents are a flowing home to immense numbers and types of tiny drifters: krill, larval crabs, jellies and one-celled plants. They swirl in clouds through the sea, small and light enough to drift without sinking, or keep afloat with bristles and fins, like seeds that sail the air.

Copepods eat and are eaten

These tiny darting animals are called copepods (the smallest look like dust specks). They eat plankton—and are in turn eaten by larger drifters.

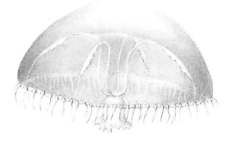

Jellies appear mysteriously

Sometimes these umbrella jellies cluster by the thousands. Other times and places there are none to be found. Like many ocean drifters, they come and go unpredictably.

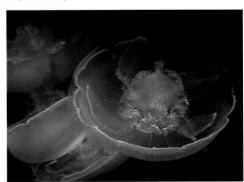

Young jellies break loose

Small, young moon jellies attach to stalks that are found stuck on rocks. Many tiny drifters spend only part of their lives at sea and the rest of their lives sitting on the ocean floor.

The Outer Bay

The outer bay is full of drama

An hour's sail from shore, the outer bay stretches for miles, and seems much the same wherever you look. But dramatic events can shatter the sameness: a school of tuna zooming past, a shark exploding a ball of anchovies, a storm whipping the waves to froth.

Ocean sunfish
Mola mola

Swift swimmers travel these waters

Many of the animals here are large, swift and strong: schooling tuna, sharks, dolphins and whales. Superb swimmers, they travel far to find rich patches of food and places where they can reproduce.

In the Outer Bay ...

Predators are many; hiding places few

Most animals here are predators

Tuna are hunters that rove in schools, using speed and sharp senses to find prey. But they're not the only hunters in the outer bay. The fishes and squid that tuna eat catch smaller prey, which catch even smaller prey. Only the tiniest drifters here are vegetarians.

Instead of hiding, some animals grow too big to be eaten

When ocean sunfish are small and young, they make an easy meal for larger fishes. But they grow very quickly, and soon they're beyond bite-size. An adult sunfish is too big to be eaten by most other fishes—the largest are 10 feet tall and weigh more than a ton!

Tuna, sunfish and sharks pierce the boundless blue

Imagine yourself floating in the middle of open water… you're suspended in a seemingly endless world. Animals appear out of the blue, then disappear again, swimming strongly or drifting on invisible currents.

Their home is wide open

The animals here don't have homes like those that live closer to shore. There are no sheltering forests of kelp—the only plants here are microscopic. There are no holes to crawl into, no reefs, no rocky retreats. Animals here live in the open; their home is the wide, clear water.

Market squid
Loligo opalescens

Ocean sunfish
Mola mola

Blue shark
Prionace glauca

Pelagic stingray
Dasyatis violacea

Imagine yourself suspended in the middle of open water

Imagine diving into the waters of the outer bay … you're far from the shore and far above the bottom. There's no seaweed for shelter here; no rocky reefs to rest upon; nothing but endless blue water around you.

Life here looms large

Many of the animals in the open ocean are large, swift and strong, like tuna and sharks. Others pass by more slowly: a flat pelagic ray; a circular ocean sunfish that flaps along placidly. Yet lots of life drifts by without notice: plankton that's too tiny or too transparent.

Ocean sunfish
Mola mola

This fish sculls slowly with its two big fins, using its stumpy tail to steer. The sunfish doesn't need to be fast to catch its meals—it eats jellies and other slow-drifting prey.

diet: jellies, other invertebrates
size: to 10 ft. (3 m)

Pacific bonito
Sarda chiliensis

This small tuna has to swim to breathe. As it moves, oxygen-rich water flows in its open mouth and past its gills. If it stopped swimming, it would suffocate.

diet: fishes, squid
size: to 3.5 ft. (1 m)

California barracuda
Sphyraena argentea

A barracuda's sharp teeth make this fish a terrific predator. Small fishes have something to fear, but you needn't worry; no matter what you hear, this fish won't bother people.

diet: fishes
size: to 4 ft. (1.2 m)

Green sea turtle
Chelonia mydas

A sea turtle swims for much of its life. It's suited to life at sea: its shell is streamlined and smooth, and it has broad swim flippers instead of feet.

diet: sea plants, jellies
size: to 4 ft. (1.2 m)

Yellowfin tuna
Thunnus albacares

Yellowfin tuna prefer tropical temperatures, so the only time they visit the outer bay is when

strong El Niño currents bring warm, tropical water to Monterey Bay.

diet: fishes, invertebrates
size: to 6.5 ft. (2 m)

Soupfin shark
Galeorhinus galeus

True, this shark has the sleek look and sharp teeth of a predator. But like most sharks, it's dangerous only to its prey. (Of the 360 kinds of sharks, only four are truly dangerous.)

diet: fishes, squid
size: to 6.5 ft. (2 m)

Swimmers

Swimmers travel far and wide

From the outer bay clear across the Pacific Ocean, powerful swimmers like tuna and sharks move freely through the sea. Many migrate thousands of miles between feeding and breeding grounds, completing the same trip many times in their lives. Always in motion, some swimmers don't stop till the day they die.

Swimmers suit their water world

All swimmers—from large, solitary sharks to small schooling fish—are fit for life in the open waters. Keen senses help many find far-scattered food; swift bodies help both hunters and hunted survive. And shimmering silver or sea-colored hues help disguise their bodies in a world full of blues.

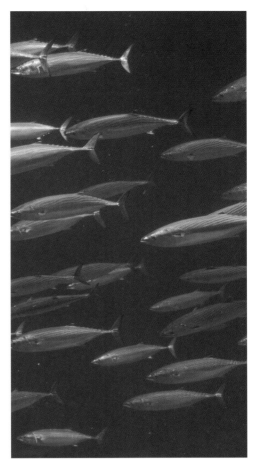

Sleek swimmers roam the open seas

Many swimmers can traverse the oceans to find the richest food patches and best places to breed. For daily travel, they cruise at a steady, efficient speed—but they can summon great bursts to overcome swift prey.

SWIMMERS

Pacific mackerel
Scomber japonicus

They spend their lives swimming

Swimming endlessly, schools of mackerel travel along our coast, covering hundreds of miles a year. Built for speed and distance, mackerel are related to some of the fastest fishes in the sea. Their torpedo-shaped bodies are smooth and streamlined, and they waste little effort as they swim.

133

Swimmers

How do they swim?

A ray flaps its winglike fins.

A tuna beats its tail from side to side.

A sea turtle paddles its flippers.

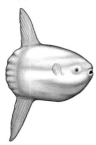

An ocean sunfish rows along with its long fins.

Animals swim with different parts of their bodies

Red muscle is used for endurance swimming.

White muscle is used for bursts of high speed.

Warm blood revs up the muscles, stomach, eyes and brain.

A torpedo-shaped body can slide through water.

What's the best shape a swimmer could be in?

It's not easy to move through water. But a sleek-bodied swimmer has an advantage. Its streamlined body can slide through water more easily than a bulky body can.

A swimmer's body shape gives you a clue to how fast it can move: a streamlined tuna goes much faster than a round ocean sunfish.

A tuna has the power to go very fast

A tuna can fold most of its fins down into grooves in its body. This ability to become "super-streamlined" makes the tuna one of the fastest fish in the sea.

SWIMMERS

Staying together's their way of life

Like synchronized swimmers, sardines in a school move together as one. This communal lifestyle's good for small fish. When predators come near, there's safety in numbers. And when it's time to reproduce, there's no need to seek out mates—plenty are close at hand.

Pacific sardine
Sardinops sagax

Are sardines following a leader?

Schooling sardines often look like they're following a leader, but they aren't. When the school turns, the fish that led the ranks end up on the flanks.

Many swimmers school together

Look for the spots on their sides

Biologists think the spots on sardines' sides help the members of a school move together. By watching the spots on the fish around it, a sardine can stay with its schoolmates.

Swimmers in schools confuse a predator's eyes

Though you might think it'd be easy for predators like sharks to catch fish in a school, it's not. A predator can't just open its mouth and catch fish. It has to use its eyes to track the fish it wants to eat, and then zero in on it.

When a fish swims in a school, it's harder for a predator to follow with its eyes, and that makes it harder to catch.

How do fish hide in a world with no hiding place?

Most open sea swimmers have two-tone camouflage: dark backs and light bellies to help them blend in. How does it work?

When a predator looks down on a two-tone fish from above, the fish's dark back blends in with the dark depths below. And when a predator looks up at the fish from below, the fish's light belly blends in with the sunlit waters above.

135

Exploring the Outer Bay

*Stretching out from Monterey Bay are
the wide-open waters of the outer bay. There's
much to see here, and much to learn.*

Discover a world outside the bay

Head out to sea and find its ever-changing nature; dive down to see what's under the surface; explore the small wonders hidden beneath the water.

Purple-striped jelly
Pelagia colorata

◄ *These dolphins
travel in huge groups.*

The Bay and Beyond

A huge canyon shapes the outer bay

Monterey Bay itself is just a small notch in the coast. But below the surface, a huge canyon descends nearly two miles down and runs 60 miles out to sea. The canyon and the outer bay make homes for the inhabitants of two different worlds.

Some live near the surface, where sun, wind and currents make it a bright and ever-changing place. Others live in the still, dark depths, far below the reach of light.

What's under the outer bay

The undersea canyon of Monterey Bay is as deep as the Grand Canyon; it descends nearly two miles and stretches 60 miles out into the Pacific. The largest undersea canyon along the west coast, it's a slice of the deep sea close to shore.

Exploring the Outer Bay: Under a Lens

Where's the life of the outer bay?

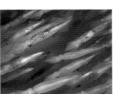

Scanning the open waters of the outer bay, you won't see much life—a soaring bird, or maybe a whale's spout. Even if you could look under water, you'd be lucky to see a school of squid or fish; large animals are only an occasional sight here. Mostly, it looks like empty water.

There's more to life than large animals

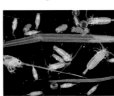

If you sailed out with a microscope and dipped into that empty-looking blue, you'd get a whole different impression: the water's swimming with life. Microscopic plants, tiny copepods, inch-long krill—these tiny beings are the most common living things in the sea, and they feed many animals in the ocean.

Exploring the Outer Bay

Soaring birds and diving whales

This water sparkles with hidden life

Big animals like whales and birds put on a good show. But in the outer bay, they're a small part of the larger picture. The true stars are the plant plankton. These microscopic plants are dazzling in their sheer numbers. Charged by the sun, they grow by the billions and supply the food that makes all other life in the outer bay possible.

The outer bay sustains life at all levels

Living things in the outer bay share a common bond: all are joined in a chain of eat-and-be-eaten. Predators, like birds and whales, feast on other animals, like fishes and squid, that in turn devour others, from anchovies to krill. Ultimately, all depend on a single source of food: tiny plants that form the first link in the bay's food chain.

The tiny drifters' world comes to life under a lens

Tiny drifters are hidden from view

The outer bay's full of drifting plankton, tiny plants and animals too small to see without a microscope. Some of the drifters spend their whole lives in the currents; they never grow too large to be carried along. For others, drifting's just a phase. Sea stars, crabs and others drift when they're young, as larvae, then settle down as adults.

Some plankton drift only as youngsters

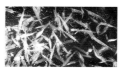

Some animals live as drifters only during the earliest stages of their lives. They start out tiny, and as they grow, they change dramatically. The adults no longer drift—they settle on the bottom or live as swimmers.

Some plankton spend their whole lives drifting

Some animals spend their entire lives drifting as plankton. Animals have to be small or light to be carried by the currents.

Drifters in the bay

Plankton—the drifters of the sea—occur in unpredictable times and places. The plankton found in the bay is always changing. What's in the bay today might be gone tomorrow.

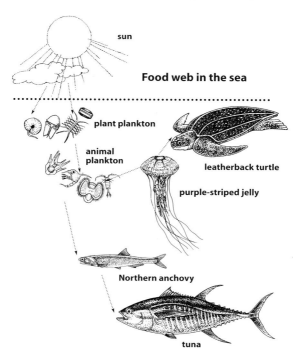

sun

Food web in the sea

plant plankton

animal plankton

leatherback turtle

purple-striped jelly

Northern anchovy

tuna

Exploring the Outer Bay: Below the Surface

From shore, all you see is the surface

If you look at the outer bay, you'll see wide water sparkling blue in the sun, or gray under stormy skies. But that's just the very surface—a tiny, flat part of an immense, three-dimensional world. To understand the outer bay, you have to go below.

Below the surface, the world changes quickly

Dive down from the surface. The farther down you go, the less it feels like a world you know: the surface waves die down; the light fades to black. The water grows colder as you descend. Life around you changes, too. Plants live only up in the sun; animals you saw near the surface are different from those below, in the dark.

From the surface down, different animals live at different depths

Surface water, sunlit water, deep sea: each has its own conditions for life

The waters of the outer bay, and the life within them, change as you descend. The influence of the sun, wind and waves is strong near the surface, but quickly falls away. Very little light reaches deeper than 300 feet down. Below that is the deep sea, a world of constant darkness.

Blue sharks patrol the surface waters of the bay. Despite their large size, the sharks feed mostly on squid, small fishes and tiny shrimplike krill.

The **by-the-wind sailor,** a relative of the jellies, floats at the surface with its tentacles dangling. Its sail catches the wind, sending the animal sailing across whole oceans.

Kelp plants that tear loose from their rocks can tangle together and float for miles. Fishes flock to these mats of kelp, which give rare shelter in wide-open waters.

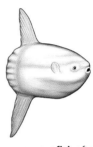

The **ocean sunfish** often basks on its side at the surface—that's how the fish earned its name. As it lies there, seagulls swim over and pick small parasites off its skin.

The **common murre** is a seabird that dives for fishes. It swims like it flies, by flapping its wings. Murres can dive 400 feet down, and stay there four minutes or more.

141

Diatoms are microscopic marine plants. (These are magnified about 500 times.) Like all plants, they need sun to grow, so they live only in the ocean's sunlit waters.

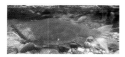

Salmon are born in rivers, but then they go to sea. Their life in the ocean's mostly a mystery. They eat and grow for about four years, then return to their rivers to breed.

Jellies drift with the currents, but they can swim as well. Many jellies travel up and down, swimming toward the surface in the evening and back down when day breaks.

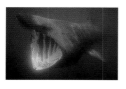

The **basking shark,** like large whales, eats very tiny food: small drifters like copepods and krill. The shark swims along, mouth open wide, and sieves food from the water.

This **siphonophore**—a jelly relative—stretches out in the deep sea and waits for prey to come. Small drifters like krill blunder into the outspread tentacles and are caught.

Lanternfish live in the deep by day. But each evening, huge schools swim toward the surface. They feast on small surface drifters, then descend before dawn.

These little animals are **krill.** By day they live in the deep. But they eat plant plankton that grow near the surface, so each night they might make a round trip of 2,000 feet.

Pelagic barnacle
Lepas sp.

Barnacles sail the outer bay

Barnacles are ocean-going animals. They live cemented to solid objects—but the objects they're attached to float loose in the sea. The barnacles fish as they drift, combing the water with feathery legs to catch their tiny prey.

What are those feathery fingers?

Barnacles don't have fingers, but they have legs. The legs comb the water to catch food, then pass it to the mouth hidden inside the shells.

How do you count barnacles?

Every long neck with a shell is one single barnacle. Each barnacle began as a tiny, drifting larva that found a float, then attached and grew.

Market squid
Loligo opalescens

Young squid get pushed around; adults make their own way

Newly hatched squid are smaller than a grain of rice. They drift at the mercy of the currents, probably staying near the surface. When grown, squid are powerful, strong-swimming animals, able to jet between the surface and the deep.

Which way's forward for a squid?

If you watch a squid in motion, it moves both backward and forward. Which way's which? A squid's tentacles are at the front end.

Squid jet back and forth

Squid can move as fast backward as forward. They're jet-powered: squid squirt out water ahead or behind to move in the other direction.

Exploring the Outer Bay: Out to Sea

Sail across the outer bay—and discover its hidden drama

From shore, the outer bay looks like an endless expanse of blue water—seamless and unchanging.

But out at sea, it's a different story. Currents twist and turn, winds wax and wane, sea life abounds, then disappears. It's an ever-shifting scene, richer and more dynamic than it appears from shore.

There's a new show every season

Explore these waters over time, and you'll come to recognize a larger pattern: the outer bay changes with each passing season. Fishes and other animals respond to these changes, marking the seasons with their comings and goings.

Sail away into the wild blue yonder

Head out beyond the shallows of Monterey Bay and a vast expanse of open water will surround you. At first, the broad vistas are breathtaking. But after a few miles, it all seems the same—nothing but endless blue.

There's something new at every turn

Slowly, though, the outer bay reveals its secrets: a jelly drifts by in the currents; a school of tuna races past. Suddenly, a flock of birds wings by overhead. And you realize there's more going on than you first imagined.

The outer bay changes color with the season

When spring and summer winds blow across the outer bay, they stir up nutrients from below. Those nutrients fertilize microscopic plants, which grow so fast and in such numbers they turn the water green.

When the winds die down in fall, the nutrients sink and the plants grow more slowly.

Clear water flows in from offshore—and the bay turns blue again.

Fall

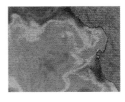

During fall, the outer bay is usually clear and blue.

Spring and summer

During the growing season, plant plankton color the water with their sheer numbers.

You can judge the bay by its color

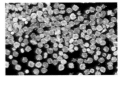

The water in the outer bay isn't a constant shade of blue; it changes from place to place and from season to season. At times, it's downright green.

Clear blue water is almost barren of tiny plant plankton. It lacks the essential nutrients the plants need to thrive—and when the plants die back, the outer bay turns crystal blue.

Murky green water is full of life. Nutrients in the water fertilize the plants, which grow in great abundance and turn the outer bay green.

Exploring the Outer Bay

Satellites see the bay in full color

When you look at the outer bay, you see an endless expanse of blue. But when a satellite looks at the bay, it sees things differently: multicolored waters that range from deep blue to pea-soup green. Why the difference?

A satellite's sensors can detect differences in floating plant life that we can't see. Even a few plants can make a satellite see green.

There's more to the outer bay than meets the eye

A satellite's view

The blotches of color on this satellite image represent different concentrations of plant plankton. The green areas are chockfull of plants; the blue areas aren't.

Animals come and go as temperatures rise and fall

Temperature swings keep animals on the move

Water temperatures in the outer bay are 50 to 55 degrees on average. But when warm water rolls in from offshore, the thermometer can rise another 10 degrees. Animals like tuna and turtles respond to these temperature swings, swimming in and out of the bay as conditions change.

Ocean sunfish can't survive in water that's much colder than 60 degrees. That's why you don't often see them in the outer bay. Look for them in August and September, when warm water flows in from offshore.

Tuna migrate thousands of miles each year, commuting on warm currents across the Pacific. When these currents flow into the outer bay, you'll find schools of tuna traveling with them.

Leatherback turtles ride warm currents all over the Pacific. The best time to see them in the outer bay is in late summer and fall, when the water's at its warmest.

Salmon travel widely across the outer bay—though you'll often catch them in cold water. There, they gorge on schools of anchovies and squid that prefer the cooler temperatures.

Market crabs thrive along the Pacific coast. Their developing young grow up in the cold currents near shore, where they find plenty of food—and later, a place to settle.

Phalaropes visit the outer bay in fall, when they migrate south for the winter. Look for them in places where cold water meets warm. There, they feast on krill and other animals caught between the currents.

Exploring the Outer Bay

Satellites sense seasons across the outer bay

Satellite pictures show how surface water in the outer bay changes temperature from season to season. Surprisingly, the water's coldest during spring and summer.

Spring and summer
(March-July)

In spring and summer, temperatures in the outer bay often drop into the 40s. That's when driving winds push warm surface water offshore, allowing colder water from below to rise up in its place.

Fall
(August-October)

When coastal winds subside in fall, warm water from miles out in the Pacific flows into the outer bay. Still, 65 degrees is about as warm as it gets.

Winter
(November-February)

During winter, a north-flowing current sweeps into the outer bay, bringing relatively warm water close to shore. Temperatures range between 50 and 60 degrees.

Why is the water colder near shore?

The answer is wind. When it blows down the coast, it pushes the bay's warm surface water with it; then, the earth's rotation carries the water offshore. The result? Colder water from the depths rises up to take its place.

A windy day

Strong winds keep the bay's warm surface water offshore and draw cold water up from below.

A calm day

When the winds die down, warm water flows back toward shore and spreads across the bay.

Ocean winds keep plants and animals in constant motion

Winds leave their mark on the outer bay

When steady winds blow across the outer bay, they stir up swirling currents of water. Jellies and other drifters get caught between the currents, marking the surface with distinct bands of life. The bands lure fishes and fishermen alike, who recognize them as prime feeding sites.

Bands reveal the interplay of wind and currents as the wind streaks across the ocean's surface.

Strong winds blowing across the ocean churn surface waters into foam—and sweep up drifting plants and animals.

By-the-wind sailor
Velella velella

This animal's built for smooth sailing

Most of the year, the by-the-wind sailor travels far out at sea; its tiny sail catches the breeze, while its gas-filled float bobs along the surface. But in spring and summer, when strong winds blow toward shore, the animal capsizes and washes up on the beach.

By-the-wind sailors often travel in large fleets. When the wind blows them near shore, you'll find millions of them shipwrecked on the beach.

The by-the-wind sailor belongs to a group of animals called "hydroids," which are closely related to jellies and sea anemones.

By-the-wind sailors breeze through life

Most animals in the outer bay either swim or drift. But the by-the-wind sailor takes a different approach. It floats along the water's surface, catching the breeze with its short, stiff sail.

Ocean Travelers

The bay's a haven
for world travelers

*If you sailed to the outer edge of the bay,
you might see some of the seabirds, tuna,
turtles or whales that swim through here every
year. Like the rest of us who visit Monterey,
these world travelers find clean waters
and bountiful food in the bay.*

Does the sea still offer safe
passage—or has it become a
hazardous highway?

While people can travel for pleasure, ocean
animals travel strictly on business; they've been
migrating to survive for thousands of years.
But lately, the world has changed around them.
Oil slicks, plastics and mile-long nets now loom
in their path. Still, it's not too late for us to turn
the tide.

Brown pelican
Pelecanus occidentalis

◄ *Humpback whales
migrate between their Arctic
feeding grounds and tropical
breeding grounds. Some
migrate to Hawaii and some
to Mexico; a few visit both
sites in different years.*

Ocean Travelers

Gray whales take the Coast Highway

Every year along our coast, people grab binoculars or get on boats to watch an amazing parade: the gray whales passing by on their annual migration. In late fall the grays go south to Mexican lagoons, to breed. In spring they pass by Monterey Bay again, returning to Arctic waters to feed.

By protecting our waters we can grant them safe passage

Seventy-five years ago, it would have been hard to find a gray whale here; they'd been hunted till they almost disappeared. Finally, people set laws to protect them. Today there are as many gray whales as ever.

But whales still need our help to survive. If we protect their ocean highways, we'll be able to enjoy them for years to come.

These waters offer whales one of the world's best habitats

Each year, thousands of whales—blue whales, gray whales, orcas, humpbacks and others—travel through the open waters of Monterey Bay.

But how do you identify an animal that's mostly under water? Scientists and whale-watchers use clues: the different shapes of the whales' tails, backs and "blows."

Blue whales have broad tail flukes

If you go whale-watching in summer, you might catch the rare sight of a blue whale flipping up its tail as it dives down to feed.

Humpback whales leap out of the water

Humpbacks come here to feed on schooling fishes and krill from April to December—the best time for whale-watchers to see them in the act.

Heart-shaped "blows" tell you it's a gray whale

Gray whales migrate through Monterey Bay twice a year. Winter's the best time to look, from a boat or with a telescope.

You can tell an orca by that tall dorsal fin

Orcas occasionally come into the bay to feed on animals like seals and young gray whales. You might see them if you were to take a whale-watching boat out on the bay.

Whales belong to the world

When whales like grays, humpbacks and blues leave Monterey Bay, they may travel thousands of miles, to Arctic or tropical seas. The same is true for many kinds of fishes and birds. Even if we protect these animals here in the bay, how can we keep them safe through all of their ranges?

The world has to agree to protect them

A whale doesn't know when it's left the boundaries of a sanctuary or crossed from one country's waters to another's. Since whales, birds and other migrating animals don't recognize divisions between nations, nations need to unite and agree to protect them.

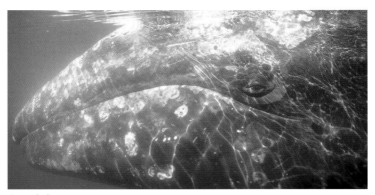

Gray whale

Nations agreed to stop the whaling

A group of whaling nations joined together in 1946 to study whales and agree on rules for hunting them. In 1986, as whales grew rare and people protested, the nations voted to end commercial whaling. The whaling ban has helped, and now whales like the humpback are starting to recover.

It's hard to agree—and to keep on agreeing

International agreements like the whaling ban are hard to accomplish, and they're always subject to change. Some countries now want to lift the ban on catching certain whales. To keep the whaling agreements strong and all the nations obeying, the public must continue to speak out for the whales.

The United Nations sets up international agreements like the ban on deadly drift nets

The world has agreed on a few other measures to protect the oceans. In the 1980s, a deadly new kind of fishing began. High seas drift nets, some of them 40 miles long, threatened the survival of many marine animals. In 1993, the United Nations banned these nets in the Pacific Ocean.

Another treaty limits marine pollution

Oil, plastic garbage, toxic chemicals and sewage dumped from ships can all damage the ocean and the animals that live there. An agreement called MARPOL, signed by 70 countries, sets limits on what ships can dump overboard, and bans plastic dumping completely.

Agreeing is never easy

It's hard for the world of nations to agree on laws of the sea. Each country has its own desires and needs. And once there's agreement, it's hard to enforce rules on ships that operate far out at sea.

Tomorrow depends on today's agreements

With more and more people in the world turning to the sea for food, shipping and waste disposal, our effect on the ocean is growing ever larger. Many marine animals are in danger, and ocean habitats are being destroyed. To save the oceans we share, we all need to work together.

Great schools of tuna visit the outer bay in fall

Citizens of the world, albacore tuna travel tens of thousands of miles in a season, circling the Pacific between here and Japan. Constantly swimming, they eat on the run. In the fall, albacore tuna come by Monterey Bay and, if the water's warm enough, bluefin and yellowfin tuna come too.

But will there be any tuna for tomorrow?

Today, fishermen take whole schools of tuna out of the ocean to meet the demand. Are Pacific tuna in trouble? Scientists don't yet know—but it's clear that in the Atlantic, tuna fishing's been so heavy since 1970, the bluefin tuna catch has dropped by 90%.

Since tuna travel the world, local laws can't protect them. The problem's a global one—and calls for global solutions.

Ocean Travelers

In 10 years there'll be a billion more people to feed—and already the fish can't keep up with the demand

Since 1950, the world population has doubled—and the world fish catch has quadrupled trying to keep up with the growing demand for food. But there are only so many fish in the sea. If we keep catching them faster than they can reproduce, we'll fish them out of existence.

The world news today: we're running out of fish

All around the world, fish are in trouble—and that means trouble for us, too. We're reaching the limits of what the ocean can supply.

But the news isn't all bad—we can learn from the past. Where nations are funding research and setting limits, the fish are beginning to recover.

Bad News— Halibut nearly vanished from tables

In just 40 years of uncontrolled fishing, the number of halibut dropped dramatically.

Good News—Halibut's back on the table now

Governments limit the number of halibut that can be caught in a year, so enough will survive for the next year.

Bad News—Peruvian anchoveta down 75%

In just five years of fishing for anchoveta, the catch dropped 75%, from 240,000 tons in 1985 to 60,000 in 1990.

Good News— You can help save fish for the future

Congress will respond to your concerns if you write or call. You can also join a group working to protect the ocean.

Bad News— Atlantic bluefin tuna under pressure

Because tuna fishing is uncontrolled, the bluefin population is only 10% of what it was estimated to be in 1970.

Good News— Maine lobsters have a long future ahead

Because laws regulate the number of traps set and the size of lobsters caught, there should be enough lobsters for years to come.

Bad News— Asia's bottom-dwelling fish decline

Here, in one of the world's busiest fishing areas, the flatfish population is down to just 10% of what it was at its highest level.

Good News— Aquaculture holds out hope

Recent successes in farm-raising mussels, flounder and shrimp mean that fishermen don't need to take so many from the wild.

Tuna nets catch dolphins, too

Fishermen usually catch more than just what they're fishing for. The example of dolphins and tuna is well known: fishing for yellowfin tuna, U.S. fishermen used to catch 100,000 dolphins a year, because dolphins and tuna swim together. The dolphins got tangled in the nets and drowned.

But now most dolphins can escape

The public's anger spurred the fishing industry to develop safer nets and fishing techniques, and today many fewer dolphins are killed. After netting a school of yellowfin tuna, fishing crews help the dolphins escape before hauling in their catch. In 1992, U.S. fleets killed fewer than 500 dolphins.

Tons of turtles, birds and fishes are caught in nets meant for other animals

Dolphins aren't the only animals caught accidentally by fishing fleets. Birds, turtles, seals, sharks and hundreds of kinds of fishes are caught, unwanted, in nets and on hooks. These animals die and are thrown back overboard.

Some nets snare whatever's there

Some ways of fishing are worse than others. Drift nets snare whatever swims in, often catching two rejects for every wanted fish. And trawls are dragged blindly along the ocean floor. Shrimp trawlers in the Gulf of Mexico discard 10 pounds of ocean life for every pound of shrimp they catch.

Seabirds dive into nets

When seabirds catch fish, they can get caught in nets and drown. Black-footed albatross feed on large schools of squid in the North Pacific—the same squid that fishing boats pursue. In 1990, drift nets meant for squid caught more than 4,000 black-footed albatross.

Changes can make a difference

Changes in the way we fish can save many seabirds and other animals. In Monterey Bay, sooty shearwaters once drowned by the thousands in nearshore gill nets. When new laws moved the gill nets out of the bay, away from where the shearwaters fed, many fewer birds were caught.

Sharks are victims, too

Blue sharks are also accidental victims of fishing nets and lines. No one knows how many sharks are killed this way, or how we might go fishing without catching them. But one thing's certain: like whales, sharks reproduce so slowly that even a small catch can have a large impact.

We need to find ways to fish without wasting animals

It is possible to fish with less waste. By changing the times or places we fish, using different gear or fishing by different methods, we can kill fewer animals by accident. The survival of species like sharks may depend on us making such changes.

Thousands of pelicans flock to the bay

Around the Monterey Bay, you might see brown pelicans flying low in spring, summer and fall. (In winter, they fly south to nest in Mexico and southern California.) But just 20 years ago, the pelicans that nested in southern California were threatened with extinction from the chemical DDT.

Twenty years ago, pelicans were struggling to survive

Farmers had used DDT since 1940 to kill crop pests. But when the pelican population plummeted, people began to ask questions. Scientists found that DDT went from field to stream to ocean—and into the fishes that live there. When birds ate the fishes they got sick and laid eggs with thin shells. The eggs broke before the chicks could hatch.

In 1972, people lobbied successfully to ban DDT in the U.S. Now the pelicans and other birds are recovering.

Ocean Travelers

Oil spills large and small are dangerous for animals

Those big oil spills you hear about on the news are just a small part of the problem. A lot of the oil that ends up in the sea actually comes from land. If your car leaks oil—or if you pour your old motor oil down the drain—the oil washes out to sea where it can poison marine life.

What happens when oil washes into the sea?

Fish eggs

Just a thin layer of oil on the water can kill the fish eggs floating there. Then sardines and other animals that eat fish eggs don't have enough to eat.

Seabirds

When seabirds like murres dive down through an oil slick, the oil coats their feathers—and then the birds can't stay warm enough to survive.

Seals

Young seals have fluffy fur that keeps them warm. But oil will mat and clump their fur, making it hard to stay warm enough to survive.

Sea turtles

When oil flows into the sea, it forms slicks and tar balls. A sea turtle that swallows tar balls can choke or even starve.

What can you do to help?

- Recycle your motor oil at a gas station.
- Keep your car well-maintained and leak-free.
- Use less gas and oil; carpool or bike to work.

The ocean needs our protection

Humans create hazards for life in the sea. Especially near shore, marine plants and animals may encounter dangerous chemicals like oil and DDT, or floating plastic that chokes and entangles. Their homes may be disturbed by drilling or dumping. Is there no sanctuary in the sea?

Monterey Bay is a marine sanctuary

There are protected places along our shores. In 1992, Monterey Bay was named a National Marine Sanctuary—one of more than a dozen sanctuaries along the U.S. coast. The sanctuary covers 5,300 square miles, stretching from near San Francisco to south of San Simeon.

The sanctuary's for wildlife

Within the marine sanctuary, wildlife and their homes are protected from many of the human uses that could harm them. There's no oil drilling allowed here; people can't mine for minerals or dump their wastes.

The sanctuary's for people, too

A sanctuary's like a national forest. It protects a natural area and everything that lives there, but it's also for people's use and enjoyment. People can still use the bay in much the way we always have—for fishing, research and recreation.

Managing the sanctuary's a balancing act

People are drawn to the beauty and rich resources of Monterey Bay. The sanctuary's goal is to protect the bay in balance with people's needs. By watching how human uses affect the bay—and halting the uses that harm it—sanctuary managers can keep this resource healthy for generations to come.

Science helps weigh the choices

To protect the sanctuary, we need to know more about it. Scientists study the rich life and nature of the bay to better understand its complex ecology. What they learn will help us balance human uses with the animals' need for a healthy habitat.

Monterey Bay's a safer place

Today, the Monterey Bay National Marine Sanctuary is a safer place for animals that live here and for those that migrate through. In creating the sanctuary, we have committed to keeping it safe into the future.

It's up to us to keep it that way

Creating the sanctuary was just the first step. Now it's up to all of us to watch over this place. We need to make sure it's managed well, to raise our voices if we see abuse, to help set policies and guidelines that will make this the best sanctuary for nature—and for people—that we can imagine.

Every August, sea turtles visit us to feast on local jellies

As summer ends, leatherback turtles swim into the outer bay to feed on their favorite food: jellies. When they leave, they head to Mexican beaches to nest and lay eggs until February. But where they go all spring and summer is a mystery, till they show up here again. It's the same with the green sea turtles that visit once in a while: Monterey is just a stop on a journey we know little about.

Sea turtles are in a race for survival

In places where thousands of turtles once came to lay eggs, now there are a few hundred. And as the world population grows, people build houses on the turtles' nesting beaches, eat turtles for food and hunt them for their eggs and shells.

Sea turtles roamed the ocean for ages with only their shells for protection, but now they need more: our attention.

Sea turtles can mistake plastic for jellies, their favorite food

Leatherback sea turtles love to eat jellies. Unfortunately, plastic bags blow into the ocean—from beaches, boats and garbage barges—where they look just like jellies to a hungry turtle. When a turtle swallows plastic, its intestines get clogged. Since the turtle can't eat, it starves.

What can you do to help?

- Buy items packaged in less plastic.
- Recycle and reuse plastic containers.
- Promote recycling in your community.

Plastic is useful, durable—and deadly

Sea turtles searching for jellies mistakenly eat plastic bags, which can kill them. And that's just one of the problems with plastic. Seals strangle in discarded fishing nets, birds get caught in six-pack rings, fishes die from eating plastic pellets. The sea is choking on our debris.

We dump it, but it doesn't go away

It's easy to think of the ocean as the perfect dump. But our garbage—especially plastic—doesn't just disappear. It floats across oceans, collecting where currents merge, washing onto our shores. There are so many of us, dumping so much stuff, we're overwhelming even the ocean's vast capacity.

OCEAN TRAVELERS

Ocean Travelers

Plastic is forever

More and more of our garbage is plastic, and once that plastic's in the ocean, it doesn't go away. It floats or sinks to the bottom, causing problems wherever it is. Plastic can take 500 years to break into little pieces, and it never entirely disappears.

It comes from everywhere

Where does all this plastic come from? We toss it. Boats dump garbage; cargo ships and fishing boats discard gear; plastic trash we throw away on land can make its way to the sea. It's now against the law to dump plastic from boats, but there's so much afloat it still causes problems.

Clean up a beach!

What can you do about garbage way out at sea? Clean up a beach close to your home! Clean-ups keep trash out of the ocean: in one day, volunteers picked up 1,754,914 pieces of plastic. And if you join an organized clean-up, they'll use data on the trash you gather to push for better disposal laws.

Want to do more to help?

If you live near the coast, there's plenty you can do. When you're out on the water, stow your trash; don't throw it. Adopt a beach or stream and work to keep it clean. Join a group that's trying to protect your local waters. And spread the word so others learn, too.

Less plastic at home means less in the sea

Think about the things you buy—is there a way to purchase less plastic? You can avoid disposable plastic items and things that are packaged in layers of plastic. And you'll encourage plastic recycling if you buy things made of recycled plastic (look for the label) as well as things you can recycle.

Think before you throw it

Think, too, about the things you throw away—could they be recycled instead? Or reused for another purpose? Are your balloons, plastic bags or six-pack rings likely to end up in the ocean? And remember when you throw something "away"—on this small planet, there is no "away."

Monterey Bay, Home and Highway

Some animals visit from season to season; others live here year-round

Monterey Bay is both home and highway to thousands of whales, seabirds and other animals. Gray whales pass by our bay twice a year; tuna and turtles visit when the water's warm. The bay's just one stop for these global travelers, but for dolphins, seals and others it's a year-round home.

Migrating animals find a good meal and a marine sanctuary in Monterey Bay

From season to season, ocean travelers join the local residents to feast on the rich marine life here. It's that very richness—and the relatively healthy habitats—that prompted people to turn the area into a national marine sanctuary. The sanctuary stretches from just north of San Francisco to San Simeon, and stresses wise resource management.

Some animals live here year-round

Some locals, like harbor porpoises, stay near the beaches. Common murres nest on islands and rocks, but spend the rest of the year on the water. Further out—a few miles offshore—swim groups of Dall's porpoises and five different kinds of dolphins.

Gray whales travel 12,000 miles a year

Each year, 20,000 California gray whales pass by Monterey Bay. In spring they swim to icy seas near Alaska to feed; in winter they return to warm Mexican lagoons to breed.

Elephant seals have babies here

Elephant seals come ashore at Año Nuevo twice a year, to mate in winter and molt in spring and summer. Traveling thousands of miles to feed, they range from Baja California north to Alaska.

Brown pelicans visit for a summer feast

From spring through fall, pelicans fly in single file over the waves off the Monterey coast—or dive, to catch anchovies. They fly south in the winter to nest in southern California and Mexico.

Sooty shearwaters arrive in thousands

Go out in a boat in spring or summer and you might see flocks of these dark birds sitting on the waves. World travelers, they fly all the way from Australia to feed along the Alaskan coast.

Orcas are on a gourmet tour

In spring and fall, groups of orcas, or killer whales, visit the Monterey Bay for a meal of harbor seal or gray whale. The rest of the year they roam the coast from Alaska to Baja California.

Blue whales eat all along the coast

Blues visit the bay in the fall. They come to eat, gulping tons of shrimplike krill. All summer and fall blues feed along the California coast, and in winter and spring they're seen off Mexico.

Leatherbacks come by for a meal

Leatherbacks visit the bay in early fall when the water is warmer to feed on jellies. Scientists know they nest on Mexican beaches, but they don't know how far they swim or where they go from there.

Albacore tuna circle the Pacific

In the fall, albacore speed through the outer bay, following warmer currents and migrating fishes. These tuna swim 11,000 miles a year as they circle the Pacific, returning to spawn off Japan.

Take Action

Each of us can make a difference

There are things you do every week already, like recycling, that help take care of the ocean. Each time you add a new habit—from picking up plastic off the beach to picking up pens to write Congress—you're making a better future for the ocean. Join us and do something more for the ocean.

Protect The Ocean Every Week

Changing the oil in your car?

Take the old oil to a disposal center to keep it out of the ocean. Each year, the amount of oil that flows into the sea from storm drains and other runoff is 22 times the *Exxon Valdez* oil spill.

Gardening or cleaning the house?

Reach for safe alternatives to harmful home and garden chemicals. When pesticides and caustic cleaners like shower and tile cleaners drain into the sea, they can harm and even kill marine life.

Free this weekend?

Call 1-800-COAST4U to find out about beach clean-ups on the California coast. Getting trash off the beach can prevent tragedies—like that of the sperm whale that died on an East Coast beach, her intestines blocked by plastic pop bottles.

Join a group working to protect the ocean

Groups like the Monterey Bay Aquarium, the Center for Marine Conservation and the local Save Our Shores work for ocean-saving laws like the one that created the Monterey Bay sanctuary.

Write your senator now

Congress makes many decisions that affect the ocean, and your representatives want to know what you think. Pick up a pencil and tell your senators how you feel about the state of the ocean.

Otters and other endangered species need your help

The Endangered Species Act protects 1,350 species of plants and animals, including the California sea otter. The act has protected the sea otter's habitat from oil drilling and other activities that cause direct harm to sea otters.

Endangered animals, plants and their habitats need continued protection to recover. Get involved in protecting endangered species.

The Clean Water Act is under attack

The Clean Water Act has protected waterways, wetlands and coastal areas from pollution, sewage and toxic chemicals for 23 years. It has protected the homes and nursery grounds of many important marine animals. It has also improved the quality of water in places we swim and fish and even the water we drink.

On May 16, 1995, the House of Representatives weakened the Clean Water Act dramatically. Get involved in protecting water quality.

More than half of U.S. fisheries are overfished

Fisheries on both coasts are in trouble. One of our richest fishing grounds—the Grand Banks off New England—has been closed to fishing because overfishing severely reduced fish stocks. The crash of cod, haddock and flounder populations cost that region 14,000 jobs and $350 million in lost revenue.

Fish stocks can recover if we have ecologically and economically sustainable fisheries management. Find out about the state of fisheries where you live.

MONTEREY BAY AQUARIUM

Dear readers,

We're concerned about the ocean and how human beings are affecting it.

We believe:

- The ocean is a place of wonder and beauty; the ocean is also essential to our survival.
- The ocean's health is endangered by pollution and overfishing.
- Pollution and overfishing are increasing as our world population continues to grow.
- All of us have the ability and responsibility to change this trend by using resources like oil less wastefully and by slowing the growth of our population.
- Protecting the ocean will bring us all rewards.

Every action we take can help protect the ocean—from picking up plastic off the beach to picking up pens to write Congress. Come join us and do something for the ocean.

Julie Packard
Executive Director, Monterey Bay Aquarium

Index

Photo and Illustration Credits

Balthis, Frank Balthis: 145 (middle center), 150 (top)

Bavendam, Fred: 24 (middle left), 27 (middle)

Browne, Rick/Monterey Bay Aquarium: 15 (top right), 36 (left), 43 (top right), 66 (2nd from top left), 69 (bottom center), 96 (top), 153 (top left)

Bucich, Richard: 55 (bottom)

Carlson, Kirsten/Monterey Bay Aquarium: 5, 9 (top), 29 (top), 35 (top), 43 (top), 55 (top), 63 (top), 71 (top), 119 (top)

Caudle, Ann/Monterey Bay Aquarium: 1 (middle), 3 (bottom right), 4 (middle), 9 (bottom), 10 (bottom left), 12 (top center, top left, middle right, bottom center, bottom right & bottom left), 13 (top left & middle center), 16 (middle center & middle bottom), 17 (middle center, middle bottom & bottom right), 18 (top left & middle center), 19 (bottom right & bottom center), 20 (top right, 2nd from top center, top left & bottom center), 21 (middle center), 24 (top right), 30 (middle left), 31 (middle left), 33 (top left, middle center & bottom right), 36 (middle center), 37 (top right, top left & bottom right), 38 (top center, bottom left & bottom center), 39 (bottom right), 40 (top left, middle left, middle center & bottom right), 41 (top center & bottom right), 45 (middle center, bottom right & bottom left), 47 (top right, top center, middle left & bottom left), 57 (top right & bottom center), 58, 59 (middle left), 60 (middle), 63 (bottom), 64 (top, middle left & bottom left), 65 (top right, top left & middle center), 67 (top right, top left, middle right & middle center), 68 (top right, bottom right, bottom left & bottom center), 78 (bottom left), 82 (middle right, middle left & middle bottom center), 84 (middle left), 85 (bottom left), 90 (top left), 91 (bottom left), 93 (bottom), 97, 101 (middle), 110 (2nd from top), 111 (top & bottom), 112, 113 (top & bottom), 121 (bottom), 122 (bottom), 123 (middle), 124 (bottom), 129 (middle), 131 (bottom left), 132 (bottom center), 134 (bottom & 3rd from top left), 135 (top left), 137 (right), 140 (top left), 141 (bottom right), 144 (top center), 147 (top right), 151 (middle center & bottom left), 152 (3rd from top left & top center), 155 (bottom right & bottom left), 156, 161-168

Chamberlain, Marc: 76 (bottom left)

Cruttenden, Carla: 72 (bottom left), 80 (middle left), 89 (top)

Eyre, Randi/Monterey Bay Aquarium: 152 (top left), 153 (bottom right), 154 (top left & bottom left)

Fierstein, David: 138 (bottom)

Folkens Pieter A./Monterey Bay Aquarium: 108 (middle)

Foott, Jeff: 1 (top), 3 (top), 24 (middle right), 74-75 (top right), 80 (middle left & top), 85 (middle center), 88 (bottom), 92-93, 94 (middle right, top left & top right), 95 (bottom), 98-99, 100 (top), 101 (bottom & top), 102, 106 (bottom right), 109 (top & bottom), 110 (top), 111 (middle right), 113 (middle), 116 (bottom), 136-137, 142 (2nd from top left), 144 (2nd from top left), 148 (middle left, middle right & top right), 149 (top), 150 (bottom right), 155 (3rd from top center & top)

Glantz, Dale: 151 (middle left)

Hall, Howard/HHP: 60 (bottom), 110 (bottom), 142 (4th from top left), 150 (middle right)

Illustrations from *A Field Guide to Pacific Coast Fishes of North America* © 1983 by William N. Eschmeyer, Olivia Walker Herald, Howard Hammann, and Jon Gnagy. Reprinted by permission of Houghton Mifflin Company. All rights reserved: 12 (top right), 13 (middle right, top right & bottom right), 19 (2nd from top center, 3rd from top center & top center), 20 (3rd top center), 21 (2nd top right & bottom right), 29 (bottom), 31 (bottom, middle center & bottom center), 32 (top center), 33 (bottom center, bottom left, middle left & top right), 38 (top right), 40 (bottom center & top center), 47 (bottom center, bottom right, middle center & top left), 49 (bottom), 51 (bottom center, bottom right, middle center, top center & top left), 52 (bottom left, middle center & middle right), 53 (bottom), 59 (bottom), 78 (middle left)

Ingram, Kris/Monterey Bay Aquarium: 96 (bottom & 3rd from top left)

Kells, Valerie/Monterey Bay Aquarium: 13 (bottom left), 17 (top center), 20 (bottom left), 47 (middle right), 69 (bottom left), 80 (middle right), 140 (bottom), 142 (top center & bottom left)

King, Jane/Monterey Bay Aquarium: 39 (bottom left), 44 (middle left), 56 (middle left), 61 (middle left), 68 (top center), 74 (middle left), 109 (middle), 128 (top left), 154 (bottom right)

Kopp, Kathy/Monterey Bay Aquarium: 41 (top right), 108 (bottom), 151 (top right)

Langstroth, Libby and Lovell: 82 (bottom left)

Light, Michael/Monterey Bay Aquarium: 65 (top center & middle right), 68 (middle left)

McCann, Andrea/Monterey Bay Aquarium: 46, 78 (3rd from top left), 127 (middle), 131 (2nd from top left), 132, top center & middle right), 134 (2nd from top left, 4th from top left & bottom left), 141 (middle right), 148 (top

center), 151 (top center), 152 (2nd from top left), 153 (top center), 154 (top right), 155 (bottom center & 2nd from top center)

Monterey Bay Aquarium: 3 (middle), 4 (top & bottom), 6-7, 10 (top left & middle left), 11, 12 (middle center), 13 (bottom center), 15 (middle center), 16 (top left), 18 (right), 20 (bottom right), 21 (top center & bottom center), 22-23 (bottom), 23 (top), 24 (top left, bottom right & bottom left), 26 (top right, middle right, middle center & bottom left), 27 (bottom & top), 28-29, 30 (top left, middle center), 31 (top right), 32 (top & bottom right), 34-35, 38 (top left), 40 (bottom left), 41 (middle center), 42-43, 43 (bottom), 44 (bottom), 45 (top right), 48-49, 50, 52 (top), 53 (middle), 54-55, 55 (middle right), 56-57 (bottom), 57 (bottom left), 61 (bottom), 62-63, 64-65 (bottom), 66 (top, bottom right & bottom left), 67 (bottom), 69 (top), 70-71, 72 (top), 75 (bottom), 76 (top right & center top), 77 (middle left), 78 (bottom right), 79 (top), 80 (bottom right), 81 (top left), 82 (top right & bottom right), 85 (top), 86 (middle), 87 (top), 94 (bottom), 95 (top), 96 (middle left), 100 (middle & bottom), 103 (top & bottom), 104 (top & middle), 105, 106 (top & middle), 107 (middle), 108 (top), 110 (3rd from top left), 111(middle left), 114-115, 116 (middle), 117 (bottom), 118-119, 120 (bottom), 122 (top), 123 (bottom), 124 (right), 127 (top left), 128 (2nd from top left & 3rd from top left, bottom left), 129 (bottom), 130 (top & middle), 131 (top left), 132 (middle center & middle left), 133 (top), 134 (top right), 135 (bottom left, middle right, 3rd from top right), 138- 139 (top), 139 (middle right & middle left), 140 (middle center & top right), 141 (top center, middle center & top right), 142 (top left & middle right), 143 (top center, bottom center, top right & middle right), 144 (bottom center, top center, top left & bottom right), 145 (2nd from top left, 3rd from top left, bottom left & top left), 148 (top left), 149 (middle right), 151 (bottom center & middle right), 152 (bottom left, bottom center & middle right), 153 (middle left), 155 (middle left & middle right)

Perrine, Doug/Innerspace Visions: 24 (middle center)

Rigsby, Michael: 53 (top), 74 (top left & 3rd from top right), 77 (middle right), 84-85 (top)

Seaborn, Charles/Monterey Bay Aquarium: 8-9, 10 (middle center), 13 (middle left), 15 (top left), 16-17 (right), 17 (top right & right center), 18 (top right), 19 (top right), 20 (top center & middle right), 21 (top left & bottom left), 22 (top), 24 (bottom center), 25 (top right, bottom right & bottom left), 30 (top right), 33 (top center), 37 (bottom left & bottom center), 39 (bottom left), 44 (2nd from top right), 45 (top left, middle left & 3rd from top left), 57 (top left), 59 (top), 60 (top), 61 (top), 73 (middle), 75 (middle right), 78 (top right, top left & middle right), 79 (middle), 81 (bottom right & bottom left), 84 (right center), 86 (bottom), 88 (top), 90 (middle left & bottom left), 125 (top), 131 (bottom right), 142 (top right), 151 (top left), 153 (top left)

Silberstein, Mark: 56 (bottom)

Snyderman, Marty: 25 (top left)

Stermer, Dugald/Monterey Bay Aquarium: 116-117 (top), 119 (bottom), 132 (top), 133 (bottom), 134 (top left)

Thompson, Frances/Monterey Bay Aquarium: 2, 18 (middle left), 20 (middle left), 21 (middle left, 3rd from top right & top right), 30 (top left), 31 (middle right), 32 (middle center), 33 (middle right), 37 (top center), 38 (bottom right), 39 (bottom center), 40 (bottom corner & top right), 41 (bottom left, middle left & top left), 51 (middle left, bottom left & top left), 68 (top left), 78 (2nd from top left), 85 (bottom right), 89 (bottom & top left), 90 (bottom right), 91 (middle left), 103 (middle left), 106 (3rd from top left & bottom left), 144 (3rd from top right)

Webster, Steven K.: 10 (top right & top middle), 12 (middle left), 66 (3rd from top left), 72 (middle & bottom right), 73 (top), 74 (top right, bottom left & 2nd from top right), 75 (bottom), 76 (middle right & bottom center), 77 (top), 82 (top center), 83 (top & bottom), 84 (bottom left & bottom center), 85 (middle right), 86 (top), 87 (top), 88 (middle), 89 (3rd from top left), 90 (middle left), 91 (top & bottom right)

White, Doc/Earthwater: 146-147, 148 (bottom center & middle center)

Wilder, Randy/Monterey Bay Aquarium: 3 (3rd from top left), 44 (3rd from top left), 57 (top center), 107 (top right & top left), 120-121 (top), 123 (top), 125 (top), 126, 128 (top), 133 (middle), 142 (3rd from top left)

Wrobel, Dave: 10 (middle right), 13 (top center), 14, 15 (bottom center, bottom right, top center & bottom left), 37 (middle center), 39 (top right), 71 (bottom), 76 (middle center), 79 (bottom), 81 (top right), 89 (2nd from top right), 125 (middle left & middle right), 127 (bottom), 128 (4th from top left), 129 (top), 135 (top), 140 (bottom right & top center), 141 (bottom center & top left), 142 (bottom center & middle center), 143 (bottom right), 145 (top right), 152 (top right)

Notes and Sketches

Notes and Sketches

Notes and Sketches

Notes and Sketches

Notes and Sketches